Talking with Animals

Talking with Animals

Charlotte Uhlenbroek

Hodder & Stoughton

For my parents

First published in Great Britain in 2002 by Hodder & Stoughton
A division of Hodder Headline

A Hodder & Stoughton hardback

10 9 8 7 6 5 4 3 2 1

A CIP catalogue record for this title is available from the British Library

ISBN 0 340 82123 X

Colour Separations by Radstock Reproductions,
Midsomer Norton, Somerset

Printed and bound by Butler & Tanner, Frome, Somerset

Jackets and Endpapers printed by Lawrence Allen,
Weston-Super-Mare, Somerset

Papers used in this book are natural, recyclable products made from wood grown in sustainable forests. The manufacturing processes conform to the environmental regulations of the country of origin

Hodder and Stoughton
A division of Hodder Headline
338 Euston Road
London NW1 3BH

Contents

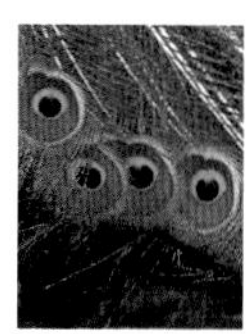
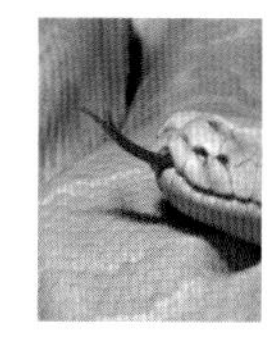
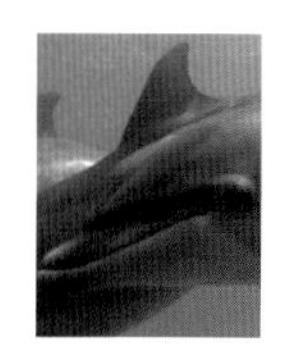

3 VISUAL SIGNALS

 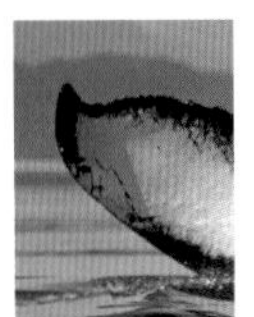 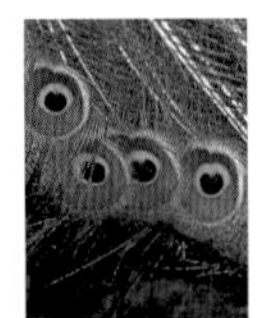 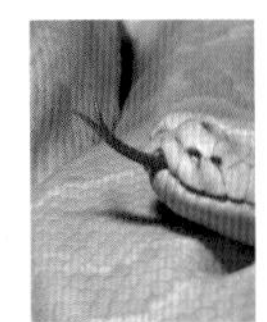 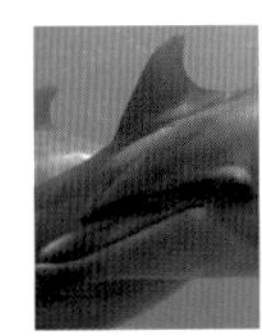 

4 CHEMICAL COMMUNICATION

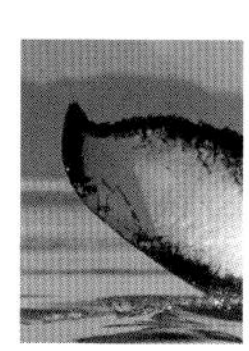

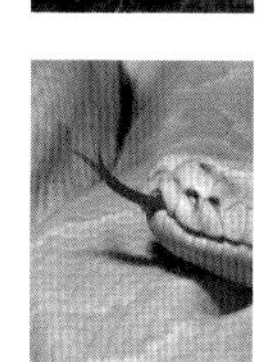

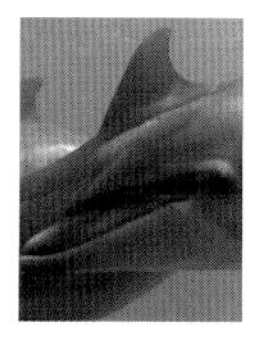

5 VIBRATION ELECTRICITY, AND TOUCH

6 LEARNING, FLEXIBILITY AND DECEPTION

1

Animal Worlds

There was never a King like Solomon,
Not since the world began;
But Solomon talked to a butterfly
As a man would talk to a man.

Rudyard Kipling

Through clouded, deep blue water, a huge shape loomed towards me. Transfixed, I held my breath while a wall of whale passed within metres of me. The adrenalin was rushing through my veins but I could also feel a deep resonant humming in my chest – the humpback whale was singing.

OPPOSITE | A tiger signposts his territory leaving deep gashes in the bark of a tree impregnated with his scent.

One moment I was just watching a small green bug on a vine leaf, then I put on a pair of headphones and it was as if a glass partition had been removed.

According to legend, King Solomon had a magic ring which allowed him to understand and speak the language of animals. Why is it that this idea has such a powerful appeal to our imagination? Perhaps it is because if we could understand them we might get a glimpse of what it is to be a giant whale roaming across the oceans, a butterfly flitting among the flowers, or a jaguar stalking its prey in the dark forest. Although we share the same physical world with other creatures, we often inhabit totally different perceptual worlds. A spider tap-dances on the delicate threads of a web, an elephant listens with its feet to vibrations coming from miles away, a fish sparks up an electrical conversation with a neighbour. All around us are parallel universes rich in smells we cannot smell, sounds we cannot hear, vibrations we cannot feel and electricity we cannot sense.

But, as technology advances, we are beginning to get unprecedented insights into the sensory world of animals. Not long ago I was given the chance to eavesdrop on a very unusual conversation: a small female stink bug was calling to her mate by sending infinitesimally small vibrations along a network of branches. This channel of communication was closed to us until very recently but now these tiny vibrations can be picked up by a laser beam, then magnified and transformed by a computer into a pattern of energy that we can hear as sound. One moment I was just watching a small green bug on a vine leaf, then I put on a pair of headphones and it was as if a glass partition had been removed. I had suddenly entered her world. I was listening to a very regular rhythm of five scratchy pulses punctuated by a pause in which came a reply from a male, pure-toned pulses followed by noisy bursts of sound – in short, a stink bug conversation. Technology can even allow us to go one step further. Using a delicate instrument called a 'mini-shaker' to tap out the same pattern of tiny vibrations on a leaf, I found that I too could call to another stink bug.

All animals communicate with one another. Communication underpins every interaction, every relationship, and puts the 'living' into life. This is because animals must be fully informed if they are to react appropriately and they also benefit from making information available to each other, whether it is a seal pup calling out to its mother on a crowded beach, a wolf marking out its territory by spraying a bush, or a fiddler crab waving its enormous claw to attract the attention of a female.

Many aspects of an animal's behaviour or appearance could be informative to others. An antelope may look sick, which tells a watchful predator that it is weak and an easy meal. A leopard may leave a trail of footprints, alerting prey as to its whereabouts. But these are incidental signs rather than signals that are designed to be informative. We can define communication as the transfer of information between animals, using special signals. Over time, ordinary aspects of an animal's behaviour or anatomical structure become ritualised or exaggerated into unambiguous signals for the purposes of exchanging information. Of course, we look at them during a particular slice of time and try to figure out what the signals mean but we must remember that communication systems are dynamic, and both signals and their meanings are constantly evolving.

One of the most basic messages which animals must convey is who they are. They must also find a suitable mate, raise offspring, defend a claim to a territory or mate, and co-operate together in groups. But if the reasons why animals communicate are relatively straightforward, why is there such an amazing diversity of signals? To understand this, we must understand the worlds in which animals live.

OPEN WORLDS

Communicating across vast distances is challenging. The Arctic looks empty – no landmarks, no sense of scale, just thousands and thousands of square kilometres of ice and snow. Polar bears are generally solitary and can travel more than 20 kilometres (km) a day in search of food. At the beginning of March the females come into season but, as they roam such distances, how do males find them? Spotting them at long range is almost impossible since they are perfectly camouflaged against the snow and a polar bear's eyesight isn't much better than ours. Even sound cannot carry far enough, as the bears may be hundreds of kilometres apart and Arctic winds can snatch away even the loudest calls. In this

Polar bears are generally solitary and can travel more than 1000 km over the course of a year across the hostile Arctic sea ice, which means finding a mate is not easy.

environment, the best way to communicate is to leave a scent message, a trail of smell that can guide males to females.

Animals often spread out in order to avoid competition for food or other resources but they still need to communicate with each other. Scent messages are widely used by reptiles and insects, as well as by mammals, to cover areas which are large relative to the size of the animal. Desert iguanas are also solitary creatures which defend territories of about a hundred square metres, the equivalent of a man patrolling an area of about 115 square kilometres (sq. km) alone and on foot. For the iguana, the best way of doing this is to leave scent marks saying 'Keep out'. But there is a further complication. In hot dry conditions, smells evaporate very quickly. Desert iguanas have overcome this problem by leaving scent marks which are protected by a waxy covering. Better still, they have special vision which allows them to see ultraviolet light so that, for these iguanas, the scent marks glow like beacons in the desert (Chap 4, p.126).

If you are a small animal in a large world, it is a good idea to make use of the environment to carry your message if you can. Smells don't have to be stationary signals and many insects use air currents to waft plumes of potent pheromones over huge distances when attracting mates. Pheromones are chemicals, secreted by animals, which exert a powerful influence on the behaviour of others (Chap 4, p.126). Some males of the silkworm family are known to follow the pheromone trail of a female for up to 48 km in the air. However, these signals can easily be lost in the wrong conditions. Moreover it is hard to home in on the exact place where the enticing chemical is coming from. Male stink bugs also use pheromones to lure females, but use a very different method of communication to locate each other precisely. They use plants as a kind of 'botanical telegraph' system, tapping out tiny vibrations which travel at speeds of 30 to 100 metres per second through a network of branches, down stems and across interconnecting roots. Other stink bugs listen in with their feet and, by assessing the strength of the signal, can move towards the source (Chap 5, p.183).

Males of the silkworm family are known to follow the pheromone trail of a female for up to 48 km in the air.

The further an animal can broadcast its signals, the greater the audience, but in some cases it is useful to be able to address a message to a particular individual. One bird has found the perfect solution, first broadcasting its message as far as possible and then, when it has attracted an audience, directing it to just one recipient. As many as fifty sage grouse (*Centrocercus urophasianus*) come together under the grey light of dawn and call in unison to summon females to the breeding areas. These are broad valleys in the huge grasslands of the north-western USA, where the low-frequency sounds carry a long way because the surrounding hills act as natural amphitheatres.

Once they have attracted the females, however, it's every male for himself. One of the problems of sound is that, generally, it isn't highly directed, but male sage grouse have found a way to overcome this. They have a pair of large air sacs in their chests which they inflate, and then squeeze, to produce their distinctive, hollow 'plop' sounds. As a male postures in front of the female he can lower and raise the sound level of these 'plops' and manipulate

their direction. If he turns sideways and offers her a view of his profile and fancy white-barred tail feathers, he can turn up the volume, channelling the sound to where the female is. When he offers her a view from the rear, the loudest sound is directed out behind him. This unique sound system certainly woos the sage grouse hens, but there is also a disadvantage in being so vocal out in the wide, open spaces where the birds are quite conspicuous: their calls may draw the attention of predators such as golden eagles.

OPPOSITE | A male sage grouse inflates the air sacs in his chest to produce loud plopping sounds. This unique sound system allows him to control both the volume and direct the sound at a particular female during courtship.

It may be risky to invite attention when out in the open, but animals that live in social groups often work together and call to warn each other of impending danger. Prairie dogs have many enemies. They live underground in a labyrinth of tunnels and are vulnerable as soon as they venture out on to the prairies to feed. They have developed a whole vocabulary of alarm calls so that they can let each other know exactly what danger presents itself and how fast it is approaching (Chap 2, p.69). Although the individual calls don't travel very far, the alarm signals are passed on from one animal to the next, creating a relay system that can carry the message much further afield.

Animals that live in social groups often work together and call to warn each other of impending danger.

Perhaps the most extensive communication network of any land animal, other than humans, is that of elephants. Elephants keep in touch with each other over miles of savannah or forest coordinating their movements in a way that seems almost telepathic. They use their keen sense of smell and lift their trunks to catch news of each other in the air, but researchers have recently discovered that elephants have another, hitherto hidden, way of exchanging messages. They produce sounds which are too low for us to hear but which can travel vast distances (Chap 2, p.32). Moreover, recent research suggests that elephants may also get news of each other by sensing vibrations that pass through the ground which cover even greater distances than low-frequency sound waves and could extend the range of elephant communication still further (Chap 5, p.188).

FOREST WORLDS

Forests are teeming with life, but you rarely see animals because of the tangle of dense foliage. In this world where many species

Out on the open steppe grasslands of North America, prairie dogs are highly conspicuous to predators. In order to survive in this environment they have developed an elaborate system of alarm calls to warn each other of impending danger.

live together in close proximity animals need conspicuous signals to get themselves noticed, but any animal that stands out can easily end up as another's dinner. Wolf spiders wander through the leaf litter sending subtle messages to each other. Females of the species *Schizocosa ocreata* leave silk woven with their scent. The scent tells a male if she is ready to mate, in which case he follows her trail. Tracking a female spider through the leaf litter is dangerous and in order to switch off her hunting instincts the male sends out minute vibrations using special organs in his forelimbs which rasp like sandpaper. So far the communication has been discreet but as he approaches the female, the male starts to dances vigorously. Using a computer-generated male spider, George Uetz and his team from the University of Cincinnati, Ohio, altered various aspects of the dance to find out exactly what appeals to the females. The males of this species have distinctive tufts of hair on their legs, and the bigger the leg tufts and the faster the movements, the more interested the female becomes. While getting him a mate, the male spider's dance often spells his doom because the same leg tufts and energetic movements also attract the attention of spider-eating toads.

If it is so dangerous to be seen in the forest, why are many forest birds and monkeys so colourful? There is always a balance to be struck between attracting the right and the wrong kind of attention. In the dense foliage, visibility is poor and animals that rely heavily on sight need to be colourful so as to be visible to each other. Many birds get around the problem of attracting unwanted attention by folding away brightly coloured feathers and crests, while guenon monkeys, which have vividly coloured masks, turn and present their dull-coloured backs at the first sign of danger. For animals that have few predators, the advantages of being conspicuous to one's fellows outweigh the risks. The psychedelic colours of mandrills in West Africa practically glow in the dim light of the forest floor and as we shall see in the next chapter, these are no accident, but have been shaped by the forest itself (Chap 2, p.39). The gorgeous birds of paradise in Australia and New Guinea also have very few predators and males are uninhibited about flaunting their amazing plumage. Perhaps most remarkable is the use of colour by their relatives, the bowerbirds of Australia and New Guinea. Instead of having their own colourful costumes, males make use of other bright and pretty things in the forest to attract the attention of females, gathering treasure troves of red fruits, yellow leaves, blue feathers, white snail shells or the iridescent outer skeletons of dead insects to adorn

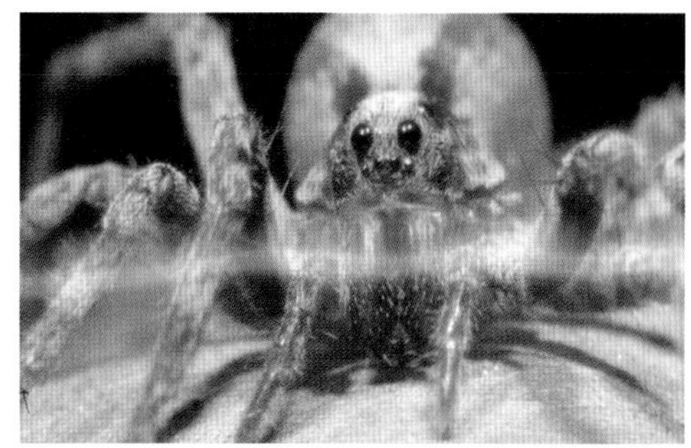

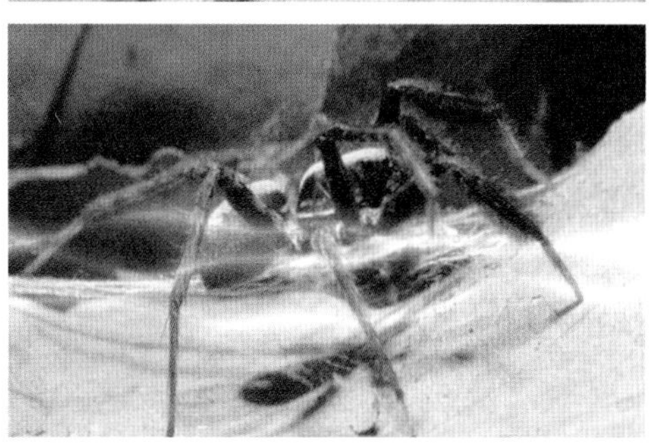

A female wolf spider impregnates a silken trail of threads with scent which tells the male if she's ready to mate. The male investigates the threads and when he finds her he 'tap-dances', sending out a special pattern of vibrations which says he is the right species. The size of his hairy leg-tufts is also important in demonstrating to the female that he is the right mate.

The vivid red of a mandrill's nose is produced by high levels of testosterone and is a mark of dominance.

their extraordinary constructions of twigs (Chap 3, p.120).

However, even the most colourful exhibition is easily obscured by dense vegetation and, for animals that want to broadcast their messages more widely, using sound is a better strategy. Several forest-dwelling primates are famous for their voices: the astonishingly loud roars of howler monkeys in Central and South America can travel more than three kilometres, cautioning other groups to keep their distance, while the lyrical songs of gibbons in South-East Asia are both an advertisement of ownership and a duet between couples to show their solidarity.

Some sounds are familiar in woodlands and forests everywhere. At dawn and dusk, forests all over the world are filled with birdsong. This is when sound carries best, but the chorus does create a problem. With so many species all singing at once, how does any one of them get a specific message across? As we shall see (Chap 2, p.39), the way in which birds sing is shaped not only by the forest environment, but also by who else is singing.

In the busy forest world, the voices of many animals compete for prominence and the competition comes not only from other species but also from rivals of their own kind. At night in the forested swamplands of southern Missouri, the clamour is deafening. It is the sound of male green tree frogs competing for females. However, because female tree frogs are actually attracted to the deepest voices, the winner isn't always the one who shouts loudest (Chap 2, p.56).

Sound is particularly important for nocturnal forest animals. Bats use sound to produce a perfect picture of their surroundings as well as to communicate with each other. In a busy place like the forest, there is always the risk of someone else picking up your signals. In most cases this is a problem for prey but occasionally the roles are reversed. By tracking prey with ultrasonic calls, bats can inadvertently give themselves away to the moths they feed on, which then take evasive action. Tiger moths go one step further, emitting their own high-frequency sounds in response and, for reasons we will discover, forcing them to abort their attack (Chap 2, p.32).

Hunters are generally very careful to conceal their whereabouts and the tiger is one of the most secretive. Tigers are solitary and although individuals rarely meet, they leave signs for each other by marking trees in the forest (Chap 4, p.139). These are deep gashes where a tiger has dragged his claws through the bark, and are usually found in a protected position. The claw marks may also be sprayed with urine, impregnating them with scent which carries a great deal of information about the tiger. So, by acting as relay stations, the trees themselves play a vital role in animal communication.

WATER WORLDS

The oceans are still a very alien realm to us. When I put on a wetsuit, buoyancy control device, air tank, mask and weight belt it often strikes me that I am kitted out as though for space travel. In fact, we probably know even less about the oceans than we do about space and what we are discovering is frequently stranger than science fiction.

Diving down, we enter a magical world of colourful corals and fishes. The majority of food is concentrated around the reefs, so animals here live together very closely and there is intense competition for food and mates. How do they know who to compete with or who to mate with? In clear water and at close quarters, bold designs and colours make fish instantly recognisable and create a shouting match of colour. It can attract the wrong kind of attention, though, and some only display their brightest colours during courtship. The blue-lipped parrotfish (*Crytotomus roseus*) flashes neon panels of gold, pink, blue and green when swooping down towards grazing females, then quickly reverts to a drab camouflage to avoid being spotted by moray eels and other predators. Colourful signals are not just used by fish around coral reefs; some squid and cuttlefish produce even more extraordinary visual displays – the giant cuttlefish (Chap 3, p.89) warns off rivals by strobing with zebra patterns, spreading out long banner-like tentacles and flushing green and crimson.

A bullethead parrotfish turns on the charm by flashing panels of iridescent colour to attract females but quickly reverts to drab camouflage if there is a predator about.

Many fish use more intimate forms of communication when it comes to courtship, often displaying and gently nudging each other near the nest site. Exchanging elaborate signals is especially important to monogamous couples who remain together. And there are few creatures that show such complete fidelity to their partners as seahorses (Chap 3, p.116). Dancing round a maypole of seagrass and swimming in parallel holding each other's tails, theirs is one of the most touching displays I have ever seen.

Showy colours and extravagant displays are useless in dark murky waters, however, and here fish have to find other means of communicating. Some use a sixth sense: electricity. Electric fish emit electrical impulses, building up a three-dimensional electrical field around their bodies. Receptors in their skin enable them to sense any distortions to this field and so create an impression of their surroundings. This ability to produce and sense electricity has developed into a means of communication among these fish, and rivers and lakes in Central and South America buzz with their electrical energy. Hiding among the vegetation along river-banks, the pintail knifefish (Chap 5, p.177) starts its courtship with sparks flying. The male and female circle and gyrate around each other while the male electrifies the water with a regular pattern of

intense impulses. With the use of highly sensitive electrodes, we are learning that several fish have a whole electric vocabulary which not only expresses their readiness to mate and their social position but can also be a warning to rivals.

Many strange creatures are found in the sea: these tunicates, or sea squirts, are abundant in the open ocean.

Another solution to communicating when there is no light is to generate your own. Sunlight doesn't penetrate further than 200 metres beneath the sea's surface and yet, some 2,500 metres down in the inky black depths, we have discovered a world of twinkling lights and glowing trails. We now realise that 80 per cent of marine creatures are bioluminescent, many tiny marine plankton and crustaceans creating swathes of phosphorescence in the water which can be experienced even by a swimmer on the surface. Swimming along suffused by light, few people realise that these tiny creatures produce the light as an alarm signal in response to their movements.

Colours, electricity and bioluminescence work only at very short range. Although our own underwater hearing is not very good, sound travels well in water, and during the Second World War the US Navy revealed that the oceans were alive with it. From the snap, crackle and pop of shrimps to the grunts, chirps and barks of fish, the high-pitched whistles of dolphins, and the hauntingly beautiful singing of whales, a whole host of marine animals use sound to send messages to each other.

CROWDED WORLDS

Thousands of dark dots spread out and coalesce, shifting shapes against a pastel pink sunset. What appears to be one fluid organism tracing beautiful patterns in the sky is in fact a flock of starlings coming in to roost. There are many places where this magical spectacle can be seen, but one of the most atmospheric is against the decaying splendour of Brighton's West Pier on the south coast of England.

Starlings, like many other birds, gather together in flocks and some of the largest of these are made up of millions of individuals. Animals that congregate in large numbers do so for various reasons. It may be in order to mate or exploit a rich resource or, perhaps most important of all, to gain protection. When thousands, even millions of animals gather together, there is potential for confusion and yet many huge flocks of birds or shoals of fish seem to move in perfectly disciplined synchrony. The spectacle of starlings coming in to roost looks like the ultimate in crowd control but in fact they avoid mid-air collisions by following a simple set of rules about alignment and cohesion (Chap 3, p.88).

The magical spectacle of starlings coming in to roost looks like the ultimate in air traffic control but is largely achieved by each bird following a set of simple rules.

Frequently, large groups of animals are not permanent but form at particular times of year, during the breeding season for instance, or under special conditions. Some of the largest animal gatherings on earth can arise suddenly. In a matter of days, locust swarms comprising over a billion individuals and covering an area of 200 sq. km can apparently appear out of nowhere. Once the swarm has formed, it acts with a single purpose, sweeping across the land in search of food and leaving devastation and famine in its wake. But how does it originate? A fascinating piece of recent research (see Chap 5, p.172) has shown that there is one irresistible signal that causes locusts to congregate in their millions, and that is touch. Indeed, it is so powerful that it literally transforms the solitary locust into a different creature.

Who has got the biggest claw? Male fiddler crabs compete to impress the females by waving their enlarged claws.

Animals which congregate in enormous numbers may still need to communicate as individuals, whether it be to advertise for a mate, identify a parent or offspring, or pass information on to others in their community. With so many others around them sending signals back and forth, it can be difficult for any one animal to get attention. There is a beach near Rockhampton in eastern Australia which is fiddler crab heaven. Thousands of fiddler crabs of various species hurry out of their burrows as the tide recedes and begin feeding on the mud flats. While feeding, the males periodically wave their colourful red claws, making overtures to the females or threatening rivals. There are some two hundred crabs per square metre and, observed from a human perspective, their frantic waving is a bit of blur. From the crabs' point of view, however, it is very different. Not only is their waving claw huge; they also have special wraparound vision which means that their claws must appear colossal, waving up and down, filling the horizon and grabbing the attention of those all around (Chap 3, p.97).

OVER PAGE | Female fur seals must find their pups among thousands of other seals who come ashore on the Pribilof Islands in Alaska.

What if animals want to be more specific than this and attract the attention of just one individual among a crowd of thousands? In July, Northern fur seals (*Callorhinus ursinus*) arrive in their thousands on the Pribilof Islands in the Bering Sea in order to breed.

The beaches are a riot of smells and sounds as bulls arrive and establish territories. Experiments have shown that among all the noise, a female and her pup who are separated are able to home in on each other's calls immediately (Chap 2, p.63). It is a bit like the 'cocktail party effect' – walk into any crowded room in which everyone is chatting and you'll be hit by a wall of sound. But should someone say your name, even quietly, it cuts through all the background noise and you are instantly tuned in to that particular sound.

Seals are forced together by their need to breed on land and there is little or no community spirit, but other animals live in groups in order to co-operate. In these communities, good communication skills are a vital part of everyday life. White-winged choughs (*Corcorax melanohamphos*) in Australia work together in extended family groups to raise their hungry chicks and have developed a way of 'naming and shaming' any individual that doesn't pull its weight. The birds live in a harsh environment and can only raise chicks if all members of the group help to incubate the eggs, defend the young and, most important of all, feed them. In return for their assistance, juveniles pick up skills and may eventually inherit the territory. But when times are hard and juveniles are hungry, they have been observed faking giving their food to the chicks so as to eat it themselves later. However, the birds have developed a policing system and any bird who is caught cheating is subjected to a 'shaming' display. On seeing a cheat, the others will puff up their feathers and wave their tail feathers slowly. Quickly all members of the group join in and the display progresses to stretching out their wings and slowly opening and closing their beaks. The final humiliation is 'boggling', by which the birds' eyes bulge out of their sockets, exposing huge scarlet orbs. Enough to put anyone off cheating perhaps but a few sly youngsters still manage to get away with it.

There is one type of society where there is total solidarity and thousands upon thousands of individuals live together in complete harmony. In the perfectly ordered world of ants and bees, pheromones are an important means of communication because one signal can be used to influence the behaviour of thousands of individuals simultaneously. What was not known until recently, however, is that ants also produce a variety of sounds that are virtually inaudible to the human ear. Rather than hearing pressure waves, as humans do, the ants sense the actual vibrations of moving air particles. It is a good system of communication for ants since their sounds don't have to travel far and noises from our world, which should be deafening to an ant, aren't heard by them at all.

Visual signals of a kind we are familiar with are also important among social animals. When living in close proximity, encounters are more often than not face to face, so it would seem a waste not to use the face as a means of communication. Rhesus macaques (*Macaca mulatta*) co-operate in groups to defend a territory. They use various calls and postures as well as some forty different facial expressions to mediate the complex and changing relationships within the group (Chap 3, p.103). One of the most common is the fear grimace. It is a way of diffusing tension and is often used by nervous animals to appease one of higher rank when they approach. Our own smile is likely to have a similar origin (Chap 3, p.105). Lip-smacking is also another appeasement signal; it involves kissing the air with small rapid movements and probably evolved from the kissing movements performed by the lips when macaques groom each other. Youngsters in the group often lip-smack to appease elders, and I wondered how one would react if I lip-smacked towards it. It was a brief but memorable exchange as the young macaque stared at me intently, rapidly lip-smacked in return and then hurriedly turned away.

I wondered how one young Rhesus macaque would react if I lip-smacked towards it . . .

As soon as we begin to appreciate the worlds inhabited by animals, we can understand why there is such a wonderful array of different signals. Among them we find some of the most alien and bizarre but also many sounds, colours, postures and expressions that have meaning for us because they are rooted in our evolutionary past. In attempting to bring the rich world of animal communication to life in this book, I have often tried to find analogies with our own lives, not only because it is easier to understand the behaviour of animals by reference to human experience, but also because it is sometimes possible to discover intriguing parallels.

2

Sound Waves

Whether it is the howl of a wolf, the whistle of a dolphin or the song of a bird, sound is one of the most pervasive and persuasive forms of communication. It grabs the attention and then disappears, making the caller conspicuous for a moment and then anonymous again. Sound is practically instantaneous, travelling in air at 340 metres per second and nearly four times as fast in water. There is a fantastic variety of sounds: dolphins produce clicks that are piercingly high and used to target shoals of fish, while the rumbles of elephants are so deep they may penetrate the ground itself and carry vast distances over the African savannah. There are also great differences in time scale: a nightingale sings a note in just a tenth of a second, producing an elaborate song at mercurial speed which we can only appreciate if we slow it down, while a blue whale takes twenty to thirty seconds to sing a single note and its song may only reach its destination, hundreds of miles away, after several hours.

OPPOSITE | A matriarch relies on her experience and memory to lead her family in search of food and water.

PATTERNS OF SOUND are almost infinite and calls can therefore encode a huge variety of different information, from the simplest to the most complex. In using sound to find a mate, look after offspring, deal with the competition, locate food sources or warn of danger, animals can send messages that are far more detailed and subtle than scientists previously realised. However, like other means of communication, sound has its drawbacks. It is susceptible to interference from such factors as wind, vegetation and humidity, and of course it draws attention to the caller from enemies as well as friends. So animals have had to develop some ingenious ways of getting their message heard by the right individuals in their own specific environments.

The vocal cords of a lion, like the strings of a guitar, produce a pressure wave which travels through the air.

THE SOUND SPECTRUM

I remember waking up in the middle of the night in a new flat in Bristol to the deep throaty roar of a lion. In that strange state between sleeping and waking I was transported back to Africa and it was some minutes of confusion before I realised that what I had heard was real. I was indeed in Bristol and hearing the roar of a lion – it was coming from the zoo nearly a mile away.

The vocal cords of a lion, like the strings of a guitar, produce a pressure wave which travels through the air carrying energy as it goes. The energy disturbs particles of air and it is these fluctuations that are picked up by our eardrums and translated into sound. Regardless of the origin, the rate of the fluctuations, or number of back-and-forth oscillations per second, will determine the frequency or pitch of the sound we hear. This is measured in Hertz (Hz) and one Hertz is equivalent to one vibration in a second. A high-pitched squeal is produced by very rapid oscillations. The intensity of energy for a loud squeal is greater than for a quiet squeal, but

A lion roars to keep other males away from his territory and his females.

the number of oscillations per second, or frequency, remains the same.

Human ears are receptive to frequencies from about 20 Hz to about 20,000 Hz but many animals can detect sounds far beyond that range. For example, dogs can hear up to about 45,000 Hz – I still find it amazing when our border collie comes hurtling over the hills in response to a dog whistle that I can barely perceive. Cats detect even higher frequencies – as high as 85,000 Hz –

while bats and dolphins use ultrasound frequencies well over 100,000 Hz.

Bats perform amazing feats in total darkness. For a time it was a complete mystery how some species could fly about in the dark, catching tiny insects on the wing and avoiding obstacles with the greatest of ease. It was not until the 1930s that the eminent Donald R. Griffin (later to pioneer the new field of animal cognition) and Robert Galambos, then working together at Harvard University, discovered how bats 'saw' in the dark. Using special microphones, Griffin found that they produce very high-pitched, or ultrasonic, sounds well above human hearing and use echoes of their calls to locate objects. He coined the term 'echolocation' to describe this navigation using sound. It is a perceptual world that is hard for us to imagine. Experiments have shown that some bats produce sounds as loud as a fire alarm, but we cannot hear them.

Experiments have shown that some bats produce sounds as loud as a fire alarm.

Echolocation is invaluable for probing the darkness and pinpointing a potential meal or gaining information about the surrounding landscape, but it also has its drawbacks. The high intensity and large number of echolocation calls produced by bats searching their environment advertise their presence and make them conspicuous to prey. It is not surprising, therefore, to find that the ears of many insects are sensitive to bat pulses. This anti-bat system provides early warning of approaching peril. Moths are among the bats' main prey and have a hearing range which easily includes the predators' ultrasonic calls. In fact moths are able to hear as high as 240,000 Hz, the highest hearing range yet discovered in the animal world. However, tiger moths (family Arctiidae) have their own defence mechanism: they emit an ultrasonic clicking sound from specialised structures on their thorax. This sound very closely resembles that of the bat's sonar. Debate continues as to whether moths are jamming the bats' echolocation system, trying to startle them, or advertising the fact that they are poisonous and make an unpalatable snack. What we do know is that when a tiger moth emits these clicks the attacking bat abruptly veers away instead of snatching its target.

At the other end of the sound spectrum are elephants, which use very low-pitched sounds to communicate over distances of several kilometres. In the great savannah lands of East Africa, a typical family herd of elephants comprises several females and their young, together with their grown-up daughters and grandchildren. These herds are led by a matriarch, usually the oldest female, whose job it is to protect and give leadership to the herd and make sure everyone sticks together. The very close social bonds between family members are immediately apparent when watching elephants. Their trunks are used not only in feeding and sensing the smells around them but are also wonderfully expressive, gently reaching out to touch and guide the young, to reassure or to greet one another after separation (Chap 5, p.164). Elephants also use many calls to keep in touch with each other and give warning if something is amiss. Trumpeting is a sound of excitement. It may express surprise or alarm, or it may be a cry for help. It can also precede an attack. The matriarch is always alert – if she senses any kind of threat she immediately becomes very protective of her family. And a matriarch defending her family makes one of the most formidable sights in the natural world. Flapping her ears and raising her trunk, she trumpets and roars in fury, and if this is not enough to scare the threat away she will charge, hurling her 3,000 kilogram (kg) body forward at speeds of 40 km/hour (25 mph).

Leadership and experience play such a crucial role in the herd that female elephants may share an extremely rare characteristic with humans: the ability to live beyond the age that they can reproduce. Other members of the herd rely so heavily on the guidance of the matriarch that if anything happens to her – if she is shot by poachers, for example – the rest of the herd mill around her body, completely disoriented, and may put themselves through extraordinary danger rather than abandon her. Her companions may even try and lift her to her feet and, if she is still alive, support her one on each side in an attempt to take her to safety.

In peaceful times, a call that is frequently used is the contact 'rumble' which allows feeding elephants to keep in touch in areas where visibility is obscured by vegetation. These are high-energy sounds of low frequency and being close to an elephant when she gives a contact rumble is a thrilling experience. From five metres away it is around 95 decibels (db) which is akin to the roar of a

OVER PAGE | The low-frequency rumbles of elephants can be below our hearing range and, as this graphic shows, travel miles across the open savannah.

At 3,000 kg an angry matriarch elephant can be very formidable.

diesel train and palpable in the air around you. In fact we only hear part of the call. The very lowest sounds we can hear are at around 20 Hz but elephants can produce a sound well below this threshold, as low as 8 Hz, which is known as 'infrasound'.

The use of infrasound may account for the seemingly telepathic way that widely dispersed elephants move in relation to each other. Low-frequency sounds travel much further than high-frequency ones – a bat's ultrasonic clicks travel less than 10 metres, a normal human conversation is discernible at a maximum of about 20 metres, while the deep contact rumbles of elephants travel more than a hundred times this distance. Just as we know the voices of our friends, family and acquaintances, so elephants recognise the voices of around a hundred others and can identify their rumbles at a range of two kilometres. If we think of it in human terms, this is like hearing the voice of a friend on the other side of a small town. And indeed the calls may carry much further than that. At night, when the air is cool and humidity decreases, even if they cannot pick up precise information, it is likely that elephants are aware of each other's rumbles as much as ten kilometres away.

It is during breeding that long-range communication may become especially important. Males gradually leave their family at adolescence, often hanging around on the periphery of the herd for a while and tagging along behind their mother, grandmother and aunts. When they reach about fifteen years of age they become independent, after which female bull elephants associate only temporarily with female groups or other males and usually wander alone. But periodically they enter a breeding condition called 'musth', when their testosterone levels increase dramatically and they actively seek out females in oestrus. Finding them, though, is no easy task. The normal range for a family of elephants is dependent on water and food availability, and it varies from 15 sq. km (6 sq. miles) in high rainfall areas to over 2,000 sq. km (800 sq. miles) in deserts. Previously it was thought that males found receptive females almost by chance, and that it was simply those males able to travel furthest who got the most mating opportunities. Now we know that males in musth are constantly listening out for the calls of receptive females, which draw them in from far and wide across the savannah lands. Moreover, some of the low-frequency sound not only travels through the air but is transmitted through the ground and may be sensed by elephants with their feet at an even greater range than airborne calls (Chap 5, p.188).

Elephants recognise the voices of others and can identify their rumbles at a range of two kilometres.

In addition to rumbles and trumpets, elephants also produce a wide range of bellows, snorts, roars, and cries. Joyce Poole has been studying elephants in Amboseli National Park in Kenya for more than twenty-five years and thinks that they may have as many as seventy different vocalisations which are used in different contexts. Many of these fall within our hearing range but others, such as the very low-frequency rumbles used at close range, especially among females and calves, we are barely aware of. Sitting with

Joyce surrounded by elephants I heard little at first, but gradually, with her guidance, my ears started to tune into sounds that were on the very edge of my senses: a murmur of sound that one only really became aware of when it stopped. There is much still to learn about the different calls of elephants, especially their long-range contact rumbles, but by far the greatest challenge will be to decipher this intimate, hidden dialogue.

It is no coincidence that large elephants produce very low sounds while small animals like bats and moths produce high-pitched sounds. In any orchestra the deepest-sounding instruments are the largest, and in general the sounds an animal makes are determined by its body size. And size not only determines pitch but volume too.

So how does a tiny creature make itself heard in a noisy world? If you put your ear to the ground by an ants' nest, it is unlikely that you will hear anything. But the ants are making noises – just too quietly for us to hear. Robert Hickling and Peng Lee at the National Center of Physical Acoustics at the University of Mississippi have come up with a solution: an anechoic chamber. This is a small soundproof room with walls, floors and ceiling padded with interlocking pyramids of foam. This produces such an extraordinary geometric effect that it feels like walking into one of those clever drawings by M. C. Escher which completely confuse perspective. There was an even stranger effect when the door was closed. The anechoic chamber simply absorbed sound. When we speak, the sounds bounce off surfaces in the environment and come back to our ears. If one of us spoke facing the wall in the chamber, although we might be two metres away from it, the sound just trailed off and died. To listen to ants and record them, you need somewhere very quiet and the anechoic chamber is the ideal place.

Ants make sounds by rubbing a set of ridges against their abdomen. Many arthropods (insects, spiders and crustaceans) are capable of producing sounds by rubbing together specialised appendages or parts of their hard outer skeleton, a process which is called 'stridulation'. So far Robert Hickling has interpreted four 'words', or commands, produced by stridulation among black fire ants (*Solenopsis richteri*). In the event of an emergency such as a cave-in of the nest, the normal, calm stridulation signals change to an alarm signal. Those ants who are actually caught in the cave-in give a different sound. This is a distress signal and is frequently combined with a powerful chemical signal, or pheromone, which calls nearby ants to the rescue. Meanwhile, if the source of the danger has been found, in the form of a human foot for example, a fourth command is issued: the signal to attack.

What is unique about these signals is that they are not sound in the ordinary sense but 'near-field sound', which is virtually inaudible to the human ear. The ants don't hear pressure waves like we and other animals do, but sense the actual vibrations of moving air particles. Near-field sound only works at very close range, which is a good system of communication for ants since their sounds don't have to travel far. Noises from further afield, such as car alarms, footsteps and music, which should be deafening to an ant, aren't heard by them at all. Instead they are tuned exclusively in to what their fellow ants are saying.

Ants sense the actual vibrations of moving air particles.

The vast majority of animals hear pressure waves and broadcast in the mid-frequency range – comparable to our hearing range. With most animals using these frequencies the airwaves can get very busy but, none the less, animals have found ways of making sure their message gets across.

GETTING THE MESSAGE ACROSS

At dawn in early May the woodlands in England are filled with birdsong. The dawn chorus has been described as a 'hymn to the dawn' and for anyone rambling through the woods as the first rays of light warm the air, the multitude of sweet uplifting voices may indeed sound like an angelic choir. But these songbirds aren't really celebrating the dawn; they are male birds asserting their claim to a territory and telling strangers to keep out. Why, then, do they choose to sing at dawn and, to a lesser extent, at dusk? There is probably a combination of reasons. It is cold and there is not enough light to get about and feed; moreover, the prey of insect eating birds is not yet active, so they might as well use this time to sing. Hormones also build up during the night so, with testosterone levels at their highest, dawn is the time when males are most inclined to seek out mates or vigorously defend their territories. The final reason why birds sing at dawn is that this is when sound carries best: it is cool, there tends to be very little wind and background noise is at a minimum. It has been calculated that a typical bird song carries twenty times better at dawn than it does at noon.

Even so, with so many birds all singing at once, one might expect individual messages to get lost. One way to avoid interference from another bird's song is to broadcast on different frequencies, rather like different radio stations. In an English woodland a song thrush (*Turdus philomelos*) broadcasts in the mid-range, a wood pigeon (*Columba palumbus*) uses lower frequencies while a firecrest (*Regulus ignicapillus*) hits the high notes at around 8 kHz.

A wren fills the forest with song, producing 103 notes in just over eight seconds.

Another way in which birds try to avoid their signals getting muddled is by having different broadcast times. Although there is no absolutely fixed order, there is a definite tendency for some species to call earlier than others. The song thrush usually strikes up well before dawn, followed soon after by a robin (*Erithacus rubecula*), a wren (*Troglodytes aedon*) and a blackbird (*Turdus merula*). Then, as the sun rises, garden warblers (*Sylvia borin*), chiffchaffs (*Phylloscopus collybita*), hedge sparrows (*Prunella modularis*) and chaffinches (*Fringilla coelebs*) all join in. Rob Thomas and his colleagues at the University of Bristol have been working on a new theory as to why the order is as it is. They have discovered that it is related to the size of the birds' eyes: those that sing earlier tend to have larger eyes than those that sing later. A major constraint on when a bird can start its daily activity is light availability, because their visual systems are primarily adapted for daytime vision. Birds with larger eyes can see better at lower light levels and so they can start their female-attracting and territory-defending dawn choruses earlier.

There is no evidence that complex songs convey any more information than simple ones but there is evidence that females are more attracted to elaborate songs. Complex songs may not transmit very well, however, so there must be a compromise. The further you are away from the source of a sound, the quieter it gets because the intensity of the energy is lost – a perfectly normal process called 'attenuation'. But there are other factors in the environment which interfere with the wave's progress, such as vegetation, wind, humidity and temperature, collectively referred to as 'excess attenuation'. Sound waves travelling through a forest are scattered by the trees and leaves, and high-pitched complex sounds diminish much more readily than low-pitched ones. This is a severe problem in tropical forests because they are often very dense and many of the leaves have a shiny surface which reflects sound. For this reason, birds living in tropical forests tend to have low, simple, repetitive calls so that their messages don't become garbled in the greenery. In temperate forests, especially open woodlands, birds are much freer to let rip and many of them do just that; a wren singing 103 notes in as little as eight-and-a-quarter seconds.

For animals that live on the ground there is an added complication. Although low-frequency sounds generally travel much better than high-frequency ones, very low-frequency sounds are absorbed by the ground. This means that there is a range of frequencies called the 'sound window', which lies between those

Chimpanzees give loud 'pant hoots' to stay in touch with others members of their community while moving about their range.

high-frequency sounds that are attenuated in the normal way by scattering and interference, and very low-frequency sounds which are attenuated by ground absorption. Sounds within this 'window' are the ones that travel best. Chimpanzees use a wide range of calls in their social interactions, but 'pant hoots' – loud, energetic calls which build up to a crescendo of high-pitched calls and screams – are the most important for keeping in touch over any distance. One type of pant hoot is usually given on the ground when chimps are travelling and the frequency range of this call fits perfectly within the sound window.

The environment can interfere with sound waves or it can be used to help animals to broadcast their messages; but by far the most remarkable sound channel is found under the sea. As we will discover, it is a unique phenomenon that allows animals to communicate with each other over hundreds, even thousands, of miles.

SOUNDS UNDER THE SEA

After moving into the Sausalito houseboat community in San Francisco, residents started to complain of a loud droning hum which was penetrating their walls and floors. A flurry of angry letters and complaints was sent to utility companies in the area, but the companies were at a loss to find the source. Those residents of a more paranoid persuasion went for conspiracy theory and decided that it was a secret government project testing surveillance equipment. After causing much annoyance and extensive detective work, the culprit was finally discovered: a small, bulbous-eyed creature called a midshipman fish (*Porichthys notatus*).

For a long time it was thought that beneath the hustle and bustle of the surface the seas were silent oceans of tranquillity. The idea was much espoused by the legendary Jacques Cousteau, the man who introduced us to the secrets of the deep, and borne out by our own experience when swimming underwater. But, the reason for this is that we can't hear very well underwater. Our middle ear is designed to pick up airborne vibrations and doesn't work efficiently when our outer ear is flooded. But if you are on a boat and drop an underwater microphone (or hydrophone) overboard and listen through a speaker, you suddenly become aware that the waters of the world are alive with sounds – popping, crackling, chirping, squeaking, moaning, growling, humming, singing.

Much of the snap, crackle and pop or 'sound of frying bacon', as it is described by many divers, is made by marine crustaceans which produce surprisingly loud sounds by stridulation. Snapping shrimps of the genera *Crangon*, *Alpheus* and *Synalpheus* are so called because they make sounds by snapping the 'finger' of a specially modified claw. This finger has a hard little knob projecting from it and the shrimps close it rapidly against the claw, which bears a corresponding socket with a small groove. When the knob hits the socket a jet of water spurts out of the groove, producing the sharp snapping sound. It is remarkable to think that a large part of the noise we can hear in tropical and subtropical waters around the world is due to millions of shrimp snapping their fingers at each other!

It was only in the 1960s that scientists first learned that fish could communicate with sound. Arthur Myrberg started his distinguished career in marine bioacoustics by studying parental care in convict cichlids (*Cichlasoma nigrofasciatum*), a freshwater fish from Central America which lavishes care on its young. One day while watching a pair in a tank at the Max-Planck Institute for Behavioural Physiology in Seewiesen he noticed something odd. The male repeatedly swam up to the female, who was busily fanning her eggs, and then suddenly turned tail and hurried to his hideout at the other end of the tank. It was only when Myrberg teamed up with Ernst Kramer, who was working as a technical assistant at the Institute, and rigged up a hydrophone, amplifier, tape-recorder and oscilloscope that they discovered what was happening. Every time the male emerged from his hiding place and got within about 45 centimetres (cm) of the female she turned round and produced a 'burrr . . . burrr' sound, evidently a warning which sent him scurrying.

Fish have a whole range of sounds – pops, grunts, burrs and chirps – which appear to play an important role in their communication, but how do they produce them? Their main instrument is usually the gas-filled swim bladder, the organ that helps to control buoyancy as they move up and down. A few fish, such as catfish and triggerfish, beat a spine-like appendage against their body wall, causing the bladder to vibrate and boom like a drum. But most fish generate sound by contracting muscles attached to the swim bladder. The design of the swim bladder, the arrangement of muscles and the rate of contraction all determine the length and pitch of a call.

Biologist Karl von Frisch could whistle and his fish would come hurrying towards him.

Before we knew that fish could pop, chirp, bark and growl there was some controversy as to whether they could even hear. Tests had shown that when artificial noises were played to various kinds of fishes underwater, they didn't react. Others argued that the artificial noises didn't actually warrant a response, because they meant nothing to the fish. It was the great German biologist Karl von Frisch, best known for his pioneering work on the waggle dance of the honey bee (Chap 5, p.197), who finally resolved the issue in a beautifully simple fashion. By training a fish to associate his whistle with food, he demonstrated without any doubt that fish could hear perfectly well and would respond if motivated. After a short time he could simply whistle and his fish would come hurrying over to him. He had perhaps rediscovered a practice of medieval monks, who are said to have rung a bell to summon the carp in their fishponds when they wanted to feed them.

Gradually we are piecing together the vocabulary of fish. Diving down to depths of only a few metres in Puerto Rico I found myself greeted by a very tranquil scene: seawhips, seafingers and deep-water gorgonians waved gently back and forth on the swell, while parrotfish and wrasse swam about leisurely or hid among the little rocky coral islands. One fish, though, seemed to be completely out of synchrony with the others, darting about in a frenzied fashion. It was the bicolour damselfish (*Eupomacentrus partitus*), a small creature about the length of a finger.

The reason for this frenetic behaviour is that males are highly territorial and extremely active in defending the area of about a square metre which includes their nest site. This is often a conch shell set in a neatly cleared patch, which the male prepares by cropping away algae and vegetation. The male damsel fish usually initiates courtship, producing little chirps of sound while swimming with his body tilted some 40 degrees and abruptly dipping down into a vertical dive. Where as female approaches, his rate of dipping rapidly increases and his colour changes to a 'black mask' pattern. He nudges the female, then leads her towards his nest, swimming with exaggerated movements of his tail and producing an occasional 'brr' sound. Sometimes the female will follow him directly to the nest and he will start to quiver while 'standing on his head', occasionally giving long chirps. The pair then swim rapidly around the nest site, their bodies almost touching while the male gives a series of grunts. At last he starts to skim the prospective spawning site, his body hovering over the conch shell. At this point the female will also start to skim, her body vibrating just above the spawning site as she begins to lay eggs. She leaves it for a minute or two while he comes in to skim and fertilise the eggs; then she returns to continue laying. Skimming and spawning can take up to two hours and while the female is laying, the male patrols around the nest site attacking anything that moves. Once they are laid he becomes the guardian of the eggs and both fans and vigorously protects them until they hatch.

During the period of incubation, any species of fish venturing within a couple of metres of his nest, even groupers and snappers

This male bicolour damselfish adopts this special 'black mask' colouration during courtship.

that are up to ten times his size, are vigorously chased away. Divers are not immune to this aggression either. We filmed one damselfish who repeatedly attacked his own reflection in the camera lens and Peter Scoones, the cameraman, and I were lunged at on several occasions with such ferocity it made us grateful that our adversary wasn't any bigger! Although with our poor underwater hearing we weren't always aware of it, these head-on confrontations are usually accompanied by explosive pops.

The discovery of just how widespread the use of sound is under the sea was made accidentally, not by biologists but by the US Navy. To enable them to pick up advance warning of German submarine attacks during the Second World War, the Americans installed a network of microphones in the sea off the East Coast of the United States. It was not long afterwards that microphones in Chesapeake Bay started picking up the ominous 'bub-bub-bub' of the approaching enemy. The US Navy was put on highest alert and began a frantic search for the German submarines, but none were to be found. Over the course of the next couple of years a pattern began to emerge – these noises were most prevalent during May and June and reached peak intensity just after midnight. After lengthy investigations, naval experts finally identified the noise. It was produced by huge schools of Western Atlantic grayling (*Micropogon undulatus*) during spawning.

Since the mid-1950s the US Navy has established an underwater surveillance system called SOSUS (SOund SUrveillance System) in order to track submarines. While tapping the oceans they have picked up some extraordinary sounds – or, as the US Navy calls them, 'biologicals' – and opened up a whole new world to us under the sea. Many loud sounds are heard regularly. One of these is Wenz's Boing, a strange mechanical sound first described by a naval expert named Wenz in the late 1950s. It is a regular winter occurrence in Hawaiian waters but even after three decades no one knows exactly what kind of animal makes it.

It has been in the US Navy's interest to assist research in marine bioacoustics, partly because naval surveillance operations have been hampered by the sounds of marine animals – on one occasion the thumping of a drumfish was apparently mistaken for a

When male dolphins form an alliance their individual whistles may converge until they are all producing the same team call.

submarine emitting an international distress signal. But marine bioacoustics also has military uses, not least for improving the navy's own surveillance and sonar equipment. Here, dolphins are top of the list as research assistants.

THE SOUNDSCAPE OF DOLPHINS AND WHALES

Dolphins produce loud clicks and listen for echoes in order to sense their environment. These powers of echolocation are remarkable. Bottlenose dolphins (*Tursiops truncatus*), for example, can detect the presence of a steel sphere only about three centimetres in diameter as far away as the length of a football pitch. Sound is also the primary means by which dolphins communicate with each other.

Bottlenose dolphins are highly social but do not live in stable groups; rather they have what are called 'fission-fusion' societies. Group membership changes by the hour, even by the minute, as individuals meet up with one another or go their separate ways, but still there are strong bonds between particular individuals that

can last a lifetime. Dolphins produce a number of different sounds during interactions – squawks, barks, squeaks and yelps – but in this fluid society one vocalisation is of particular importance for keeping in contact. Each dolphin has a signature whistle – a high-pitched sound with a unique contour which allows other dolphins to identify it. In the wild it is hard for researchers to be sure which animal is whistling, but they can get around this problem by temporarily attaching a hydrophone to each dolphin's head with a small suction cup.

Wild dolphins show that they develop their own characteristic whistles by the age of two but sometimes they borrow each other's whistles. Marine biologist Vincent Janik, of the University of St Andrews in Scotland, has been studying bottlenose dolphins in the Moray Firth. He has discovered that when one dolphin whistles its signature, other dolphins will imitate that whistle in response, presumably to maintain contact with that particular dolphin, rather like calling its name.

This mimicry and flexibility of expression indicate that dolphins have the kind of brain power that underlies speech. Using each other's whistles may also be a way in which some dolphins advertise special relationships. Rachel Smolker and John Pepper, experts on dolphin communication from the University of Michigan, followed three male dolphins in Shark Bay, western Australia, that had formed an alliance. Over several years, by analysing their whistles, the researchers found that as the males co-operated more and more closely their individual whistles became more and more similar. Eventually these were indistinguishable – instead of individual signature whistles they had developed a single team call. Smolker and Pepper suggested that having a team call is not just a way of bonding with each other, but of drawing attention to the alliance as a force to be reckoned with, making rival males uncomfortable, and perhaps attracting female dolphins.

Other marine mammals are thought to attract their females by singing. In October on the east coast of Australia migrating humpback whales pass very close to the shore. With the help of Max Egan, a technical manager from Southern Cross University in New South Wales, Australia, we went to film them near Byron

OPPOSITE | Swimming with dolphins is an extraordinary experience.

Bay. It was incredibly exciting to spot the little puffs of spray on the horizon – the tell-tale blow of a whale. When migrating, the whales can be travelling at speeds of about 12 km/hour and can dive under for anywhere between five and forty minutes, but with many years of experience Max usually guided our boat to exactly the right place to provide us with spectacular sightings. As the whales break the surface like submarines, the water spilling off their broad dark backs, huge tails, or flukes, rise out of the water, the white underside etched with individual markings. Then, with a powerful downstroke, they dive back into the depths of the sea, leaving just a smooth glassy patch of water or 'footprint' on the surface to indicate where they had been.

On one day we had travelled up and down the shore and far out to sea in search of whales, but the horizon was deserted. There was no report of whales in the area so we decided to test out Max's new, highly sensitive hydrophone and the result was astonishing. As soon as the hydrophone was in the water we found ourselves listening to the most beautiful voices. What may have seemed like a vast empty ocean was filled with the singing of whales.

It is the males which sing, as they migrate between feeding and breeding grounds. No one knows for sure what the purpose of these songs is, whether they are love songs to the females or warnings to other males to stay away, but they have a mesmerising, other-worldly quality. Like musical notes or words in a human song, whales use about twenty syllables which include cries, chirps and yups, uttered in patterns called 'motifs'. The first motif may go: 'cry, cry', the second: 'chirp, chirp, chirp'; a third: 'yup yup yup'. Two or three motifs make up a phrase, or line, and in turn, several of these make up a theme or verse. The songs are composed of several different themes and while the basic song is continually repeated, the individual phrases can vary considerably in length, which means each song can last nearly an hour. It was thought that each population of humpbacks had its own song which remained constant but recent findings (Chap 6, p.221) suggest that the whales appreciate a catchy tune and quickly adopt any new songs that they hear.

On average, sound travels underwater at speeds of 3,350 mph, more than four times as fast as in air. The speed of sound is determined by the properties of the medium through which it travels: the higher the temperature, pressure and salinity in salt water, the faster sound travels. In tropical and subtropical waters, sound travels fastest near the surface where the sun's warmth penetrates. The temperature gradient is extremely steep until you get about a kilometre down and this is where sound travels slowest. Below a depth of one kilometre, the temperature continues to fall gradually but pressure becomes a major factor in causing sound to travel faster again.

That sound travels at its slowest rate about a kilometre below the sea's surface is highly significant because sound waves are bent towards the path of minimum velocity. (It is rather similar to the effect you get when sledging down a snowy hillside. If one runner hits a grassy patch, the sledge will lurch in that direction.) This means that any sound wave will be refracted from both deeper and shallower waters and carried along a sound channel one kilometre below the surface (rather shallower near the poles). It is called the SOFAR (SOund Fixing And Ranging) channel and is one of the most extraordinary phenomena on earth. Any sound wave that becomes trapped in this channel may follow a gently undulating path for thousands of miles through the middle depths of the ocean. During the Second World War a physicist called Maurice Ewing predicted and verified the existence of the SOFAR channel. Submarine crews and downed pilots were able to send distress signals by releasing a small sphere designed to collapse at a depth of one kilometre and emit a ping which could be picked up by receiver microphones placed at a similar depth perhaps thousands of miles away. The efficiency of this SOFAR channel was dramatically demonstrated in 1960 when the sound of a depth-charge exploded off the coast of Australia was recorded 19,300 km away in Bermuda after an interval of three-and-a-half hours.

OVER PAGE | Scientists can recognise individual humpback whales because the markings on every individual's tail, or 'fluke', are unique.

Blue whales (*Balaenoptera musculus*) are the loudest animals on earth. They can sing much louder than a jet at take-off (around 190 dB whereas a jet is 140 dB and a human shouting just 70 dB) and use the SOFAR channel as an underwater PA system to send

messages halfway round the world. Unlike most baleen whales which follow regular migratory routes, both blue whales and fin whales (*B. physalus*) roam the oceans alone for long periods and then congregate at irregular and unpredictable times. In order to do this, they not only send their calls along the SOFAR channel but also produce infrasound well below the threshold of human hearing. These very low frequencies (15-35 Hz) travel great distances but, furthermore, when whales evolved this was also a 'quiet' channel, below the range of interference from wind and waves and other animal sounds. This permitted them to communicate with each other unimpeded across hundreds of thousands of square kilometres of open ocean.

A female humpback whale and her calf travel to feeding grounds in the Antarctic.

OPPOSITE | A blue whale usually roams the oceans alone but can keep in touch with others over an area of approximately 8,000 square kilometres with songs that carry along a unique underwater sound channel.

Today noise pollution from shipping traffic may be seriously hampering the whales' ability to make themselves heard. Propeller-generated noise can be as low as 3Hz, extending into the whales' private channel. Morever, it is loud. Roger Payne from Cornell University and James Hrynyshyn, a scientific journalist, have calculated that before the advent of motor engines, background noise would have been about 30 dB (equivalent to a quiet whisper), which meant that blue and fin whales could have access to each other anywhere within an area of 314 million sq. km without raising their voices. Today background noise levels have doubled and that area has shrunk to less than 8,000 sq. km. Both blue and fin whales can increase the power of their normal output to produce sound levels of almost 200 dB, about the volume of a space rocket being launched, but as ambient noise levels in the sea go on rising, it is unlikely that whales can continue to compensate by shouting. It may be getting harder and harder for males and females to locate each other and this could be a reason why many species have failed to recover from the destructive whaling era which reached its zenith in the early twentieth century, despite several decades of protection.

Whales use their exquisitely sensitive hearing to follow migra-

tory routes, locate one another over great distances, find food and care for their young. Their ability to function and survive is under serious threat if their hearing capacity is undermined by noise. As one scientist succintly put it: 'A deaf whale is a dead whale.' Sound has been shown to divert bowhead and grey whales from their migration paths, to cause blue, fin, sperm and humpback whales to cease vocalising, and to induce a range of other effects, from distressed behaviour to panic. A mass stranding of beaked whales off the west coast of Greece in 1996 has been associated with a sonar system being tested by NATO.

ARE DEEP VOICES SEXY?

During the day the swamps of southern Missouri in central USA are tranquil places. Oakwoods open out on to watery glades filled with large lily-pads, ducks and dragonflies, the squat bulbous shapes of tupelo and cypress trees emerging from the water and filtering the light with their branches. When the sun goes down, the swamps change character dramatically. Millions of mosquitoes appear, intent on blood and immune to even the most lethal repellents, while sinister cotton-mouth snakes emerge from their hiding places to hunt and all around is a steady build-up of thousands of voices from the swamps. Deep, throaty bullfrogs (*Rana catesbeiana*), high-pitched cricket frogs (*Acris crepitans*), the melancholy sheep-like 'baa' of the Great Plains narrow-mouthed toad (*Gastrophryne olivacea*), the twangy banjo of green frogs (*Rana clamitans*) and, loudest of all, the sound of the green tree frog (*Hyla cinera*), a beautiful glistening green frog about the size of a 50-pence piece.

Their evening starts with a chorus of 'stay away' calls to other males until all the competitors are approximately evenly spaced out. Then the males begin the difficult task of luring a female with whom to mate. As males go out most nights but only a few females are receptive, the ratio of male to female green tree frogs on any given night is about 50:1. The acoustic competition for these females is intense: the croaks given by the eager males are deafening. With each croak they puff up their body and then force the air out past their vocal cords into their air pouch by violently

A male green tree frog has to make his voice heard among thousands in order to attract a female. Although it uses twenty times his resting metabolism for each call, he can keep going half the night.

contracting their abdominal muscles. This requires a huge expenditure of energy – green tree frogs use about twenty times as much energy croaking than at resting metabolism. This is the equivalent for us of running at over 10 mph, and they keep this up from sunset until midnight!

Males have slightly different pitched calls and call rates. Carl Gerhardt at the University of Missouri conducted a classic series of playback experiments to discover what characteristics of the calls were attractive to females. He played different calls from two speakers and it emerged that female green tree frogs usually approach those speakers playing the calls of lower-than-average pitch and higher-than-average rates. Low-frequency calls depend on the size of the vocal cords: large males are able to produce low-pitched calls while small males must produce higher-pitched, less attractive calls. Although not correlated with size, call rate is energetically costly and only males that are highly successful foragers can sustain high rates. So females are attracted to the largest males and those most successful at foraging.

There is a twist, though, because some males do not call at all. These satellite males lie in wait near a calling male and sneakily intercept females attracted to his calls. Moreover, males shift tactics from night to night, calling or sneaking according to how much food they have had and how they are feeling! The sneaking tactic may not be as successful as calling, but males optimise their chances by sitting near callers with the most attractive, low-pitched calls.

We can tell a great deal about another person from the sound of their voice and many animals use this as a means of assessing each other. The sight of a red deer stag (*Cervus elaphus*) standing proudly with antlers held high is an inspiring one, but these magnificent antlers are not just for show – they are serious weapons and, come autumn, the stags have to prove their mettle. During the rut, only a few males will have the opportunity to breed and they fight furiously to win possession of a harem of females. On average, stags fight about five times during this period and, by the end, a quarter of them are badly injured, some permanently. In this situation it is very important to size up your opponent carefully before challenging him and red deer have evolved a very precise ritual which enables them to do exactly that. When a challenger approaches a harem holder, the two roar at each other for several minutes. Then they start to walk up and down in parallel and the tension builds until one turns and faces his opponent, lowering his antlers. They lock antlers and start to push strenuously against one another, each wrestling to twist the other round and gain the advantage of higher ground. When one starts to lose ground rapidly he disengages and runs off, leaving the victor in possession of the harem.

Many contests end after either the roaring or the parallel-walking stage. Parallel walking gives the opponents the opportunity to gauge their relative sizes and so their likely strength. But even at this stage there is danger – the stags are within range of each other's weapons and if a challenger has misjudged the harem holder he could get hurt. In fact, unequal contests are relatively rare because stags are very good at sizing each other up from a safe distance. During a long-term study of red deer on the Isle of Rhum

in the Inner Hebrides, Tim Clutton-Brock and Steve Albon from Cambridge University conducted a series of playback experiments and found that the rate of roaring as well as the pitch and quality of a stag's roar are used to express and assess fighting potential. In general, the higher the roaring rate, the lower the pitch, and the harsher the quality of a roar, the more likely an opponent is to back down. It takes energy to roar, and a high roaring rate gives an indication of an animal's stamina and motivation. However, the deepness of the roar also gives a kind of physical description of the caller, because there is a general rule across the animal kingdom: the larger the animal, the lower the pitch of their voice.

When competing over female harems, red deer stags hold ritualised contests which include roaring at each other, an effective way of sizing up an adversary before risking a fight.

Given this rule, it is likely that animals' calls have evolved in order to particularly accentuate deep sounds in aggressive situations. Highly aggressive sounds such as growls, snarls or roars tend to be low in frequency – and also atonal or harsh in quality (because of the additional energy bands that result from a loosely vibrating membrane around the glottis). On the other hand, friendly, appeasing or fearful sounds tend to be high, clear tonal sounds: whines, squeaks, whimpers, coos, etc. Although dogs do become familiar with particular sounds, more often than not it isn't the words themselves they understand but the tone of voice – just try telling your dog he is good in a gruff voice or naughty in a high-pitched one!

SHOWING SOLIDARITY WITH SOUND

The howl of a wolf seems to embody the spirit of the wild. Its purpose is to keep intruders out of the territory of the wolf pack: on hearing a stranger, members of a pack declare themselves by lifting their heads and uttering a long series of mournful howls. I was taught how to howl by wolf expert Sean Ellis. He and his wife, Jan, are now putting their knowledge of wild wolves to use in improving the conditions of wolves in captivity. What is so unusual about Sean and Jan is that in order to do this they themselves have become members of a wolf pack and so have gained a very intimate insight into wolf behaviour.

Some of the work conducted by the Ellises is concerned with

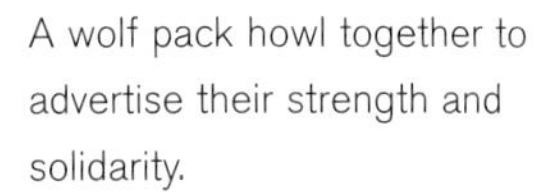

A wolf pack howl together to advertise their strength and solidarity.

playing recordings of various alien wolf packs to the pack at Longleat Estate in south-west England. As Sean pointed out to me, having several wolves in a decent-sized enclosure with plenty of food is not enough. It is external influences quite as much as internal influences that shape the social behaviour of wolves and make them into a proper pack. This is completely logical – the reason for the unity and cohesion of a pack is the potential threat of intruders.

As well as other signs such as scent marks (Chap 4, p.143) the pack relies on distant howls to provide it with information about its neighbours. A howl tells them the sex, rank, physical condition and intentions of a wolf. One study of wolves in Canada found that the howls given by a wolf who is approaching another in an aggressive manner tend to be significantly deeper than howls from stationary wolves. Lone wolves may howl, but when in a pack, if one individual starts to howl all the others join in (even the pups, often with a happy medley of barks, yips and yaps). This not only shows their solidarity to any wolves in the neighbourhood but also helps to create the impression of a large number of animals.

In a confrontation, the relative size of each pack is crucial to the outcome. When routing strangers from their land, the lead wolf will often pause to let lagging members of the pack catch up or even go back to find them before continuing with the chase. This isn't simply being friendly, but making sure he has the advantage of numbers on his side if it comes to a fight.

In fact, in many cases contests are not between single individuals but between groups of animals who join forces to defend their patch. And, as we have seen, sound is a good way of assessing the opposing force from a safe distance. Many social animals, including several primates, exchange volleys of high-intensity calls during territorial disputes, rather like teams of opposing football fans out-singing each other during a match. Indris (*Indri indri*) chase intruders out of their territory with a wall of sound, troops of howler monkeys (*Alouatta* spp) bellow at each other over distances of several miles, while if a party of chimpanzees encounters strangers on the border of their range they erupt into a cacophony of loud, defiant 'waa barks' and 'pant hoots' while drumming

furiously with their hands and feet on the pleated buttress roots of huge trees. In both cases there is evidence that the side with fewer males tends to back down.

The same is true among lions. Lion prides often roar together, advertising that they are a force to be reckoned with. Adult lionesses don't tend to differ much in body size from individual to individual, but the presence of larger, powerful males can make quite a difference to a pride's strength. Studies have shown that lions can readily differentiate between the roars of lionesses and the much deeper roars of lions and avoid groups with several males. But males may often be absent from prides and then it is left to the lionesses to protect their territory. When prides encounter one another, intense chases usually ensue which, not surprisingly, tend to be won by the largest prides. The risk of injury or death to the losers is significant, and research has shown that lionesses are very careful to assess the odds of success before engaging in battle.

Lions seem to be able to count. By hiding loudspeakers in the vegetation of the Serengeti in Tanzania and playing recordings of unfamiliar lions to a pride, Karen McComb from Sussex University found that lions compare the number of intruders against the number of their companions and only approach if the odds are weighted in their favour. It isn't in fact the number of individuals they are evaluating, but rather the volume of sound they are faced with. Not only were lions less likely to approach playbacks of three intruders than of a single intruder, but when they did approach three intruders they undertook the approach more cautiously. Lions roaring in chorus overlap their roars (one individual initiates and others join in, adding their roars in an overlapping fashion), so a single lion is incapable of producing a sound equivalent to a group of three. Because of this constraint, roaring choruses provide an honest advertisement that more than one individual is present in the group.

ENCODING INFORMATION

Off the west coast of Alaska, the Pribilof Islands are one of the remotest places on earth and even in July it was bitterly cold and frequently shrouded in fog. But there is something very special about the islands – they are home to about a million Northern fur seals (*Callorhinus ursinus*), 70 per cent of the world's population. We went to film there with Steve Insley from the Smithsonian Institution who has spent the last twelve years studying the seals' calls.

A female fur seal and her pup are able to home in on each other's calls immediately.

Peering over a cliff edge we were instantly hit by a riot of sound. Roars, growls, yells, whickers and barks accompany the fighting, bullying and bickering as bulls arrive and establish territories. The best territories are high up out of the surf and this is where females head when they arrive from the sea. But it is a journey fraught with danger – they have to get past aggressive bachelors intent on waylaying them as they come ashore. We saw a couple of females lying bloodied after being grabbed and tossed in the air. Soon after their arrival, the females give birth to the pups they conceived the previous year. The pups take a lot of energy to feed and not long after they are born, their mothers leave them for a week at a time. While the mothers are away searching for food, the new-born pups are left to look out for themselves. Throwing around their considerable weight of up to 270 kg, the bulls can easily crush them and so for safety the pups gather together in creches.

OPPOSITE | The throat sac of a siamang gibbon amplifies its song across the forest and keeps strangers away.

When a mother returns she has the seemingly impossible task of finding her pup. First she must once again run the gauntlet of sex-starved males as she comes up the beach. And then, among thousands upon thousands of growls, roars, whickers, yells and bleats, she has to hear the sound of her own pup calling. If she fails, it will starve to death. How does she do it? Steve Insley has played

back recordings of mother-and-pup calls to different individuals and has found that among all the noise the mother and pup immediately home in on each other's calls. Insley's research has shown that not only do mothers and pups recognise each other's calls out of thousands, they also recognise them over many years. But while it is critical that females and pups recognise each other the first year, it is not clear why they would need this ability over time. Perhaps this kind of vocal recognition is not unique to them. Could it be that males also recognise neighbouring territory holders from previous years and maybe even co-operate with each other to maintain their territories?

But exactly how might identity be encoded in the calls of animals? A similar phenomenon is found among king penguins (*Aptenodytes patagonicus*) that huddle together in their tens of thousands as protection against the freezing blizzards of the Crozet Islands in the southern Indian Ocean. When the penguin chicks are a month or so old both parents go to sea, sometimes as far as 500 km away, to fetch food for the growing chicks. On their return, parents and chicks relocate each other by calling. Recent research by Pierre Jouventin from the Functional and Evolutionary Ecology Centre in Montpellier, France, has shown

ABOVE | King penguins on the Crozet Islands in the South Indian Ocean breed in colonies numbering tens of thousands of individuals.

Adult penguins leave their chicks, sometimes travelling 500 km to feed out at sea. On their return the hungry chick welcomes a meal.

that there are essential cues buried within the calls which help penguins to discriminate between them. To find out where these may lie, researchers modified various parts of the parents' calls and played back recordings to the chicks. The chicks responded positively to the bass frequencies of the calls, but not at all to the high-treble frequencies. This reflects the fact, known to every midnight raver (and disturbed neighbour), that bass frequencies travel further and more efficiently than treble frequencies – especially through an intervening cordon of bodies. Moreover, the first quarter of a second (230 milliseconds) of the call was enough for chicks to correctly identify their parents. So while the calls are repeated over and over again, less than 6 per cent of the total duration of the call is required for recognition. This 'built-in redundancy' accords well with the theory of communications which says that the best way to ensure a message gets across in a noisy environment is to repeat it often.

Researchers think that a chick learns its parents' voices from a very early age and can recognise them again, even after they have been away at sea foraging for a number of weeks, by matching what it hears with a memory of its parents' calls. This is somewhat similar to our experience at a noisy rock concert when the intelligibility of the singer's words is greatly improved if you know the lyrics already.

In addition to proclaiming their identity, animals use calls to convey information about all aspects of their lives. Chaffinches have nine different calls, some of which are given in very precise contexts. A 'tupe' signals that a bird is about to take flight and causes other chaffinches to follow suit, while a 'squeak' is given only by an injured bird and must convey an immediate sense of danger to the others. Some calls are given only by particular birds. For example, one kind of alarm call, the 'tew', is unique to recently fledged birds and evokes escape behaviour. Two other alarm calls are the preserve of cocks in the breeding season. One is a 'seee' call, reserved for the sudden appearance of a hawk, while the other, a 'huit' call, means that the male is uneasy but danger isn't imminent. Both serve to alert adults and the latter also silences the nestlings. Males also have special 'kseep' and 'tchirp' calls which they use to address females during courtship, while the female answers with her own 'seep' when she is ready to copulate.

The structure of these calls is not arbitrary, but tailor-made to carry different messages. The first criterion is how far the call must carry, but other factors also influence its shape. The contact calls of many birds start with a series of simple tonal syllables which carry well and get everyone's attention, followed by the complex rapid trills which contain the actual information about the caller. This is like the town crier ringing his bell before making an announcement.

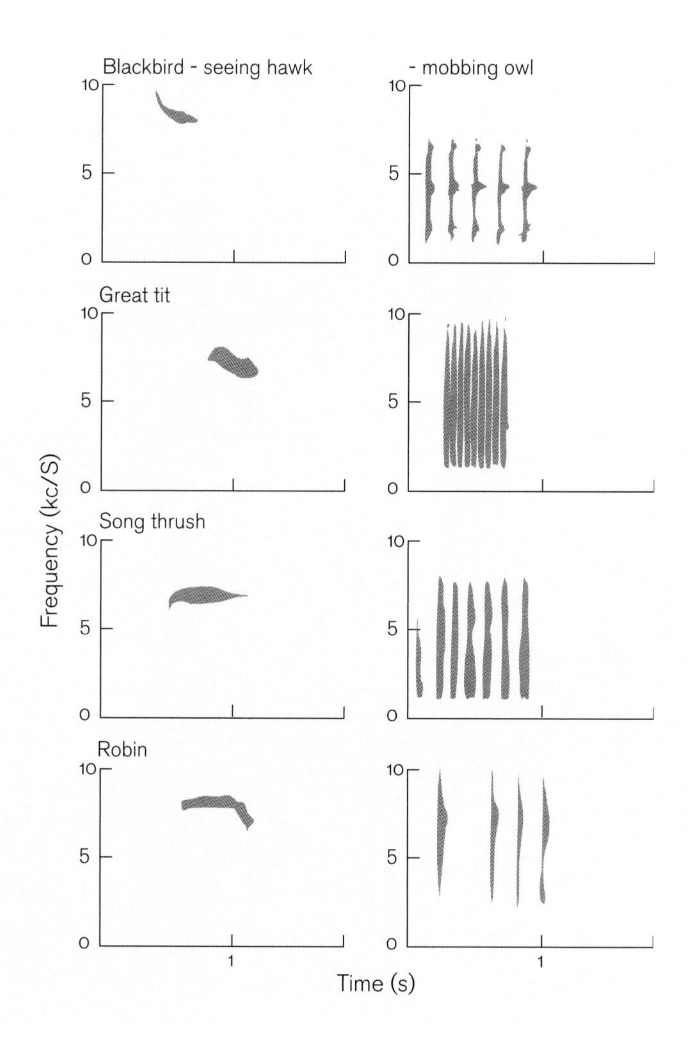

Calls of four passerine birds given when a hawk is flying over and when mobbing an owl, showing the close similarity of the calls of different species.

The alarm calls of birds are also perfectly tailored to their purpose. While they need to be attention-grabbing, the last thing a bird wants to do if it spots a hawk or another danger nearby is to alert the predator to its presence. The solution is to produce a distinctive call whose source is very difficult to locate and which not even an acoustical engineer could have improved on: the calls are high-pitched and pure-toned; they start quietly, get louder and then fade very quickly, so that they reach the ears of immediate companions but not those of the enemy. In one experiment, captive red-tailed hawks (*Buteo jamaicensis*) were placed in a wood and played recordings of the 'seet' hawk alarm of the American robin (*Turdus migratorius*) from a hidden loudspeaker. They immediately responded by rotating their heads as though searching for the source of the sound, but ended up an average of 124 degrees off target!

As this is the ideal structure, it is not surprising that many birds have come up with very similar alarm calls (see graphs), with the result that different species can 'understand' and take advantage when other species sound the alert. Mobbing calls are entirely different. Obviously when there is a predator to be got rid of it is good to get reinforcements from far and wide, so these 'Come and join me' calls have to be very easy to locate – they are loud sharp notes almost like hand-claps. Once again many species have come up with similar solutions and blackbirds, mistle thrush (*Turdus viscivorus*), robins, garden warblers, wrens, stonechats (*Saxicola torquata*) and chaffinches all understand each other's voice-prints.

SYMBOLIC CALLS

Until recently, a sharp distinction was made between animal calls and human language. Animal vocalisations were regarded as involuntary and the information contained in a call was seen as purely motivational. That is, animal sounds simply expressed the animal's internal state (fear, hunger, distress, contentment, etc.) in the same way that a scream or exclamation of surprise declares a person's emotional state. Only human speech was considered to refer to external phenomena, an attribute which has been variously labelled as 'symbolic', 'representational', 'semantic' and 'referential' by different authors. But in the last few decades clear evidence has emerged that some animals are capable of referring to things in their external environment and often with great precision.

The first concrete evidence of this came from vervet monkeys which give different alarm calls depending on the type of predator at hand (Chap 6, p.211). Such referential calls are now known to be quite widespread among monkeys and birds, even chickens. But we may have to re-evaluate our view of animal communication even further in the light of some startling new findings. Gunnison's prairie dogs (*Cynomys gunnisoni*) are small rodents and one of the most common animals of the American South-west. We were filming in a conservation area of wide open prairies north of Flagstaff in Arizona, with the deep pink of the painted desert as a backdrop. This huge, dramatic landscape looks rather empty at first, but if you stay still and wait a short time a head will pop up out of a burrow, then another and another and another, their little pointy faces looking about nervously.

Prairie dogs are on the menu for many predators, but they can't flee at every potential danger or they wouldn't get a chance to eat. Recent evidence suggests that some have developed a very sophisticated early warning system which alerts other prairie dogs to both the kind of predator and the speed of its approach.

Prairie dogs live in highly organised social groups called coteries and several of these make up 'towns' – a vast network of interconnected tunnels which can cover an area of up to 160 acres. Many cattle ranchers regard prairie dogs as a nuisance because livestock can break their legs tripping up in their burrow openings, they compete with cattle for pasture, and they can carry diseases such as bubonic plague. As a result they are regularly shot. Humans aren't their only enemies, either. Prairie dogs are hunted by a huge number of animals – coyotes, birds of prey, foxes and American badgers as well as domestic cats and dogs. Their alarm calls are very loud and can carry for distances of more than a kilometre. Recent research by Con Slobodchikoff of Northern Arizona University shows that, like vervet monkeys and birds, they have different alarm calls for different predators, which produce different escape strategies. Human and hawk alarm send prairie dogs running to their burrows and diving inside. For a human-elicited call, running to the burrows is a colony-wide response, but for a hawk-elicited call, only the animals in the immediate flight path of a diving hawk respond in this way. Coyote alarm calls elicit a running to the lip of the burrow, from where they watch the progress of the predator. But that's not all. They also incorporate information about the predator's speed of travel by shortening the time interval between individual alarm barks in a calling bout, in direct proportion to the speed of approach.

The latest analysis indicates that prairie dogs can go one step further still. They can describe individual predators in detail. For instance, they can tell people apart and even use slightly different calls in a systematic way to describe the colour of their clothes, their general size and shape, or whether they are carrying a gun. Commenting on the appearance of a potential predator not only allows other prairie dogs to assess the level of threat but also provides them with a clear search image. We are only just beginning to decipher and understand the kind of information prairie dogs are passing on to each other, but if small rodents show such an extraordinary level of sophistication, what might we find that other animals are saying to each other in the future?

Prairie dogs can tell people apart and even use different calls to describe their clothes.

NATURAL INSTRUMENTS, RHYTHM AND MUSIC

One of my favourite birds, found in many parts of equatorial Africa, is the African broadbill (*Smithornis capensis*). In Gombe National Park in Tanzania the unmistakable sound of its courtship, a funny little 'brrrr . . . brrrr . . . brrr', is commonly heard in the forest. The broadbill is a small brown bird that is usually quite hard to see as it lives in tropical forests, but the trick is to look out for movement. The sound is produced by air blowing across specially shaped and strengthened feathers as the male performs an aerial acrobatic display – launching himself off his perch, tracing a small circle in the air and then returning to his branch. He repeats this action over and over again in an attempt to attract a mate until you feel he must be quite dizzy.

Many birds produce sounds in much the same way. Mute swans (*Cygnus olor*) are so called because, unlike the other two European swans, they don't vocalise. Instead they produce a highly distinctive humming throb in flight as air passes over their primary feathers. The short-eared owl (*Asio flammeus*) also has an amazing mid-air performance in which it claps its wings together below the body. On sudden take-off the red grouse (*Lagopus lagopus*) produces an explosive whirring sound which may be designed to startle predators and buy the grouse valuable seconds to get away.

Birds don't just use their feathers to make percussive sounds; their beaks can be used as instruments too. Many owls make a rather startling castanet-like sound by snapping their bills if disturbed at the nest, and the tap-tap-tapping of a woodpecker is a familiar sound in any English woodland. Since they are essentially songless birds, woodpeckers use their hammering skills not only to seek out insects from under the bark of a tree and excavate nesting holes, but also as a kind of telegraph system, tapping out messages to other woodpeckers in the vicinity. It might seem that banging away on a tree-trunk doesn't allow for much subtlety of expression, but the woodpecker's drum-roll contains quite a lot of information. The rates of drumming within each roll and the temporal pattern of drum-rolls can both indicate what species it is. For example, Nuttall's woodpecker (*Picoides nuttalli*) has a slower rate of drumming (i.e. fewer beats per second) than the downy woodpecker (*P. pubescens*). These share the same areas in parts of California, so it is important that they can recognise their own species for communication. The length of the drum-roll can indicate sex (for example, male Nuttall's woodpeckers drum more frequently and for greater lengths than females) and within particular time brackets can even reveal the individual's identity.

Drumming is traditionally used by people from many tribes in Africa to send messages from hilltop to hilltop, but the sound of drumming can also be heard in the forests. This is not humans drumming but chimpanzees, slapping their hands and feet against the buttress roots of trees. Males drum far more frequently than females and the drumming is often accompanied by volleys of 'pant hoots' (Chap 2, p.42). When many chimps are drumming and calling together the valleys resound with sound, and local people have told stories about the revelry of chimpanzee carnivals in the forest.

Chimpanzees use drumming while travelling through their

A kakapo, the New Zealand nocturnal flightless parrot, creates a hollow 'booming bowl' to amplify its calls to females.

range to keep in touch over long distances. Research by Christophe Boesch in Tai in West Africa suggested that by drumming on a series of trees in succession a chimpanzee informs others about his direction of travel. In Gombe there are not enough suitable buttress trees to allow chimpanzees to do this, but the locations of good trees are well known to chimps and they will often make specific detours to pass by and drum on them. As a result any listener in the vicinity, including human researchers, can tell exactly where a chimp is when he drums. In Gombe I found that males also frequently drum when they are heading out on a patrol of their boundaries, which they must do several times a month to keep trespassers out. This drumming seems to act as a kind of rallying cry to other males to come and join the expedition, and as the posse moves out from the central valleys each male in turn will drum on buttress roots as he goes by.

One day I was with a male chimpanzee called Prof who had been relaxing quietly, lying on his back on the forest floor and gazing up into the canopy. His foot was resting on a piece of hollow wood and after a few minutes I was startled to hear a very quiet, slow rhythm as he tapped it on the log. I was even more amazed when he shifted position and started tapping the log with his hand. The whole episode lasted only a few minutes, but it left me wondering about the origins of music.

There is plenty of music in nature: birds and whales use rhythms in their songs similar to those in our own music, yet they could just as easily formulate free-form, arrhythmic sounds. And even though they are capable of singing over a range of at least seven octaves, they use musical intervals between their notes that are similar or identical to the intervals in our scales. Most surprisingly, the songs of humpback whales contain repeating refrains that form rhymes. This suggests that whales use rhyme in the same way as we do: as a mnemonic device to help them remember complex material. The fact that whale song has so much in common with our own music, even though our evolutionary paths have not crossed for 60 million years, raises the possibility that rather than humans being the inventors of music, music may far predate humans. Every human culture has music and apparently when the Bushmen of the Kalahari were asked about the origins of music by the writer Laurens van der Post, they looked puzzled and replied, 'Can't you hear the stars singing?'

3

Visual Signals

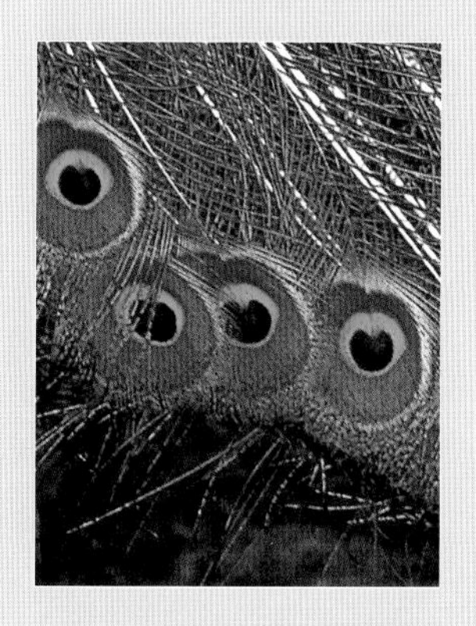

When we walk into a room full of people we are sending messages long before we open our mouths to speak. We pick up a huge amount of information about a person from their appearance – we instantly judge their sex, age, ethnic origins and general state of health. Humans rely so heavily on vision to communicate that since our early history we have augmented our appearance with a fantastic array of ornaments and embellishments, which make blatant (if not always truthful!) statements about us. Blue hair and a nose-ring send a very different message from a fur coat and diamonds. For many animals, appearance is equally important and their embellishments are no less extraordinary.

OPPOSITE | Fish see the world very differently from us. Although the yellow and blue stripes of this royal angelfish make it conspicuous to its own kind at close quarters, these colours ensure perfect camouflage at only a metre or two.

THE MAGNIFICENT FAN of a peacock's tail, the graceful antlers of a red deer stag or the outlandish red nasal balloon of a male hooded seal are not simply decorative. They can take a lot of energy to produce, they can be cumbersome, and even a liability, perhaps attracting attention from the wrong quarters. But these beautiful and bizarre adornments make strong and immediate statements to their fellows and in the animal world appearance can be everything.

Why are visual signals so important? The best reason is simply that we can see. Light from the sun is vital for life and almost all creatures are sensitive to light. We know that even single-celled creatures register light and will move towards or away from it. Complex, light-sensitive eyes which allow the perception of detailed images are widespread among more highly organised animals. Even jellyfish and earthworms have eyes – albeit of a more primitive design.

Mature male hooded seals inflate a red nasal balloon in an aggressive display to other males.

For primitive animals, the ability to see was incredibly useful – it helped them to find food, avoid danger and navigate – but as the visual sense became increasingly accurate and sophisticated it also became a good and reliable way of sending signals. And the fastest. At 300,000 km/sec. the speed of light ensures that the way an animal looks sends an instantaneous message to all those around it. But there are also distinct disadvantages with using vision to communicate: it works only at close range and bold signals can sometimes draw unwanted attention. The kinds of visual signs used by animals therefore depend not only on what their eyes can see best, but on where they are, what it is they want to say and who else might be watching.

OPPOSITE | Appearance can be all important when attracting a mate.

COLOURS AND DECORATION

Nowhere on earth is more full of vibrant colour than a coral reef. Below the aquamarine surface of tropical seas lies a magical world of coral gardens. Delicate branches of fan corals, dramatic fire corals and azure barrel sponges are home to a spectacular array of Day-Glo marine life. Brilliant yellow butterfly fish hover in pairs, glistening silversides flit and flash in shafts of sunlight, huge schools

of glowing orange anthias crowd around coral heads while parrotfish parade about in pastel blues, pinks and purples.

Why is there such a multitude of magnificent costumes in the natural world? The colours, patterns, spots and stripes of reef fish enthral scuba divers, but looking beautiful is not the primary goal. By wearing permanent 'uniforms', animals of all kinds save a lot of time and energy in stating their identity. But they do face something of a quandary when it comes to these signals. On the one hand, they want to be conspicuous to their friends and other members of their species; on the other hand, they don't want to alert predators to their presence. While the vivid colours of reef fish are designed to be conspicuous at short range, they also help to camouflage fish at a distance. We might find this difficult to appreciate but then no reef fish sees itself, or its neighbours, the way we do. Below 30 metres there is no red light and the colour vision of fishes tends to be tuned to the shorter end of the spectrum – blue and ultraviolet – and to be less sensitive to reds and yellows. Many reef fish are yellow and blue. The yellow is not seen as colour but as contrast – blue reflects light in the spectrum that yellow does not and vice versa – which makes them highly visible at close range. At a distance of only a metre or two the markings serve to break up the outline of the fish and when the bands of colour are too close together to resolve they fade to grey.

The distinctive markings of many fish, birds and mammals are especially useful when closely-related species are living in the same habitat. In the rain forests of central Africa several species of guenon monkeys have overlapping ranges and, as they are all remarkably similar in shape, size and behaviour, it is easy to see how individuals moving through the deep shadows of the canopy could get confused about who is who. But each species has evolved its own colourful mask – nose, cheeks, forehead, ear tufts or bib in white or black, rufous red, blue-grey, yellow or orange – which gives a clear signal of its identity. Among our own garden birds, finches too are very similar in shape, size and behaviour, but again each species has its own tell-tale markings on face or wings which prevent them from wasting time chasing off mistaken rivals – or, worse, making sexual overtures to someone of the wrong kind.

CLOCKWISE FROM TOP LEFT | De Brazza's monkey, blue monkey, white-nosed monkey, diana monkey, vervet monkey. These guenons are all closely related, similar in general appearance and live in the same forests in West Africa, but even in thick vegetation their distinctive face markings make them easily distinguishable.

On the savannah of East Africa, with some very dangerous predators around and practically no shelter, antelopes and gazelles have coat patterns and colours that blend in naturally with the golden browns of the grasses. Nevertheless the correct uniform remains crucially important. In Kenya's Masai Mara, this was clearly evident when a film crew recently came across a very unusual albino Thomson's gazelle (*Gazella thomsoni*). Instead of the usual golden-brown back and white belly separated by a smart horizontal black stripe, this youngster was almost pure white with only the faintest dark stripe along its side. It obviously knew it was a Thomson's gazelle and wanted to graze among the rest of the herd – a lone gazelle does not escape the attention of lions, hyenas, cheetahs or leopards for long. But because it looked different it was not welcome in the herd and was chased away time and time again. Every time it sidled in amongst them and tried to take a mouthful of grass, the others would harass it until it had little choice but to stay on the periphery, exposed and vulnerable to any danger. Even then, the rest of the herd continued to hassle it until eventually it had to move away or die of hunger and exhaustion. Not just its conspicuous whiteness but its rejection by its own species left it little chance of survival.

Occasionally a conspicuous uniform can be just what you need to avoid trouble. In human society we know the importance of giving a clear signal in hostile situations. For example, Red Cross personnel make sure they don't look remotely like an armed force in a war zone and advertise their vehicles with a bold cross on a white background. One of the more dangerous occupations in the natural world is that of cleaner fish. Several species of these little fish are known to perform the kindly act of cleansing larger fish of surface parasites, fungi or dead tissue (whilst getting a satisfactory meal for themselves, of course). The large fish form queues while waiting for their treatment. It is vital that the cleaner fish clearly indicate their special profession and they do this by wearing unmistakable uniforms which say, 'I am harmless and very useful, so don't attack me and don't eat me.' Justin Marshall, at the University of Queensland, has shown that many cleaner fish share a similar and rather unusual colour labelled 'cleaner blue'. This colour has a long-wavelength component, not visible to our eyes, which is quite different to blues in other fish. It appears to be a unique signalling colour on the reef, reinforcing the message given by the cleaner's uniform.

OPPOSITE FROM TOP | Hawfinch, chaffinch, greenfinch, bullfinch, goldfinch: each species has its own tell-tale markings which help to avoid confusion.

Even so, because of the personal danger involved, the cleaner fish approach with caution. They swim close to inspect the host and wait for it to adopt a special pose of encouragement. The Red Sea goatfish (*Parupeneus forsskali*), which is predominantly white, will hover upright and turn red to signal to a cleaner fish that it needs grooming, and perhaps to make external parasites stand out against its skin. The cichlid *Etroplus suratensis* holds its head up and rapidly flickers its dark pelvic fins while quivering its entire body to say that it has recognised the uniform and won't attack. In this case calling a truce is especially important as the client approaches the cleaner fish in its own territory, where it is liable to be most defensive.

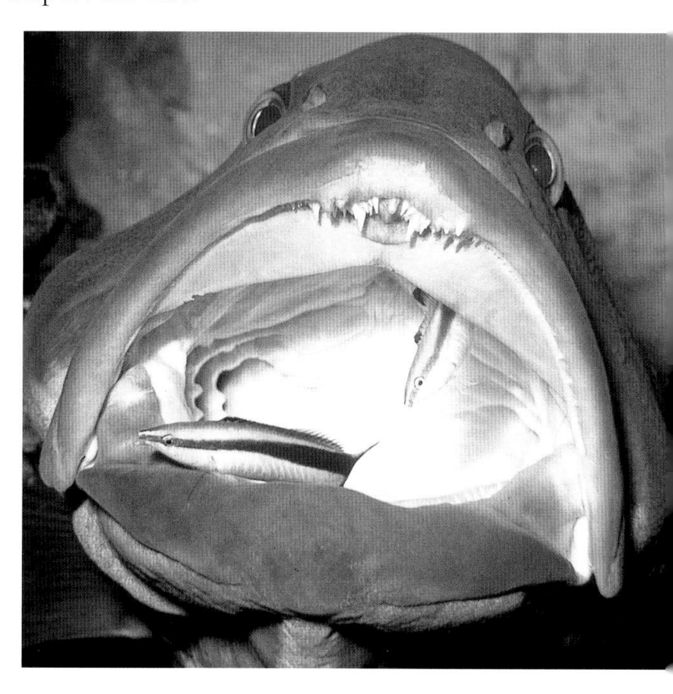

Cleaner fish risk their lives each time they clean a cod's mouth, but have a blue uniform which is highly conspicuous to other fish that says 'I'm useful, don't eat me'.

Perhaps some of these elaborate poses are a necessary precaution because some fish have jumped on the cleaner fish's bandwagon. The sabre-tooth blenny lives in the same habitat as the blue-streak cleaner fish and is a veritable wolf in sheep's clothing. It not only looks identical to the cleaner, but it also copies its swimming motion. This charade allows the blenny to get close enough to larger fish such as parrotfish to take a chunk out of their fins, or to tear off a scale, whilst being protected from predation. For this reason, it is often seen being chased about the reef by an angry parrotfish!

Other animals avoid being eaten by using colour codes that say just the reverse – 'I am dangerous!' Many frogs, toads, salamanders, beetles, butterflies and moths are poisonous and advertise the fact with what are known as warning colours. The effectiveness of

The viceroy butterfly (top) mimics the colours of the monarch butterfly in order to deceive birds into thinking it tastes horrible.

OPPOSITE | The colours of this mandrill are no accident. Primates evolved good red/green colour discrimination in order to find fruit in the forest, so the dominant mandrill's scarlet nose makes him highly conspicuous in the green vegetation.

warning colours was neatly shown by a study of a species of Lygaeid bug conducted in the mid-1980s by Birgitta Sillen-Tullberg of the University of Stockholm. This bug comes in two distinct varieties: one is cryptically coloured (that is, its colouring tends to camouflage it in its usual habitat), the other sports bright colours of red and white with black spots or bands, but both contain mild chemical toxins and are unpalatable to birds. The experiment showed that although in general great tits knew about the toxins and tended to reject both types, they handled and killed the cryptic variety far more frequently than its conspicuously coloured colleagues. And just as some fish bluff their way into a meal by pretending to be benign cleaner fish, so other animals have developed the clever strategy of avoiding predators by parading the markings of their more dangerous relatives. The viceroy butterfly mimics the colours of a poisonous monarch butterfly to tell birds that it tastes horrible. In fact it is as nutritious and tasty as any other large, non-poisonous butterfly, but its colours deceive birds.

Many warning colours are patterns of contrasting black and scarlet or black and yellow. Does this mean that these are internationally recognised warning signals among animals? The answer is probably not. What is the case, however, is that some colours and patterns are more conspicuous than others, and a common feature of all warning signals is that they have to be as bold, distinctive and memorable as possible. There is no point in giving a namby-pamby warning that will be forgotten the next time the predator gets hungry.

Many animal colour schemes are not accidental but shaped by an animal's environment. One of the most eye-catching animals is the mandrill (*Papio sphinx*) which lives in the dense West African rain forest. Not much is known about mandrill behaviour but they move through the rain forests of Gabon and Cameroon in an almost nomadic fashion. Groups of twenty or thirty individuals range over areas of 5,000 hectares and every now and again they gather in their hundreds. Although there are leopards in these

forests to which youngsters probably fall prey every now and again, mandrills are larger than baboons and if they stick together it is likely they have little to fear. Certainly they are conspicuously colourful. They have yellow beards and boldly painted faces – electric-blue muzzles smartly set off by a red stripe running down the length of their noses. These colours are so intense that when I first saw them it was hard to believe they were natural. The males are particularly bright, but the alpha male easily outshines all the rest, bearing witness to the high levels of testosterone surging through his body. The hormones don't just turn their noses crimson, they colour the skin of the whole body so that if you look closely under the alpha male's thick brown hair you can glimpse flashes of deep red. When he turns his back, he presents a rump that positively glows with psychedelic reds, pinks, blues and mauve. This unmistakable bottom and dramatic face are like a banner, a focal point around which the rest of the group gathers.

Sometimes a symbol of fighting power may become more important than actual fighting ability.

The forest itself has shaped the colour scheme of mandrills. Primates have excellent colour vision and are particularly skilled in distinguishing between red and green. The theory is that this was probably an adaptation for detecting red fruit against a green background of leaves. Our own retinas are especially good at discriminating between red and green and this plays a part in the human world – it is the reason why traffic lights are the colours they are. It appears that mandrills have capitalised on this adaptation and use the most visual signal possible – bright red – to stand out like a beacon in the green foliage.

The way an animal looks can be all-important when it comes to attracting a mate. First, though, you must be sure that you are actually dealing with the opposite sex and many animals rely on special markings or decorations to avoid mistakes. The males of the North American woodpecker, the yellow-shafted flicker (*Colaptes auratus*), have a black 'moustache' streak that the females lack. In an early experiment designed to test how important this marking is in determining how males and females perceive each other, a researcher captured the female of a pair and painted a 'moustache' on her. When she was released she was immediately attacked by her mate, who no doubt took her for a rival male. The experiment may be ethically questionable but it leaves no doubt about the potency of a small visual signal.

Many sexual signals are directly linked to health and status. The massive palmate antlers of a bull moose can stretch to around 2.5 metres across and are a clear demonstration of his vigour. Their primary purpose is as a weapon, but they are also a symbol of status. This is equally true of the antlers, horns and tusks of other ungulates. Male mountain sheep, for example, assess the size of an opponent's horns from a distant hillside and tend to approach only other rams with similar-sized horns. The various crowns and bizarre headgear worn by some lizards are another instance of using weapons to make a statement and this may have been instrumental in the remarkable armoury and ornamentation of dinosaurs such as triceratops. Sometimes, though, a symbol of fighting power may become more important than actual fighting ability. It has been argued that the sole use of the antlers of the extinct Irish elk, *Megaloceros giganteus*, was as a status symbol. With a spread of nearly four metres, these antlers must undoubtedly have been pretty impressive, but as 40-kilogram (kg) appendages to a 2-kg skull they are surely rather an unwieldy weapon!

The black bibs of male sparrows are a symbol of their status – the larger the bib the higher the rank – and in this way they avoid squabbles over females or food.

Status symbols don't have to be brash. Some, such as those used by house sparrows, are quite subtle. House sparrows often travel and feed in flocks, and males have black bibs which denote their rank. The larger the bib, the higher the rank. In groups there are always going to be squabbles over food and amenities (such as dust-baths), as well as over mates, but displaying a permanent badge of rank saves a lot of time that might otherwise be wasted in assessing others or in fighting. In sparrow society there is a strict hierarchy that keeps males as well-disciplined as an army. A flash of a black insignia is all that is required to pull rank; then small bibs immediately give way to larger bibs. Males with large bibs are more likely to secure mates earlier in the season, copulate with their mates more frequently, and to mate with other females outside their pair.

A sudden dramatic change of costume can be very effective for making an impression. Black tie or an evening dress tend to have more impact if they are not worn every day at the office, and similarly a great many birds wear their most fetching plumage only during the breeding season. This is especially true of males, which in most species have to vie for the attention of the females. In the autumn and winter the male scarlet tanager (*Prianga olivacea*) is green like the female of the species, but come spring he takes on a completely different persona and changes into a rich crimson plumage. Dramatic effect aside, there are some good reasons why these birds don't keep their special plumage all year round. The first is that it is something of a liability, making them far more conspicuous to aerial predators. The second is that by changing only for the breeding season the plumage gives a double signal – red feathers not only clearly mark the tanager as a male, they also announce that he is looking for a mate.

Low-ranked single male fairy wrens end up being recruited to look after the offspring.

Males of the superb fairy-wren (*Malurus cyaneus*) of south-eastern Australia are brown for most of the year, but turn to brilliant blue in the breeding season. The timing of this change is extremely fine-tuned and depends on each individual's social position. Males who have charge of their territories make the change fully a month before those who have no territory of their own and live within other males' territories. The special attire thus indicates a male who is not only ready to mate but is high ranking and in possession of his own territory to boot. This is so attractive to females that, with a month's head start, the highest ranked bag them all; lower-ranking males end up with little choice but to be recruited to help look after the offspring.

INTERMITTENT SIGNALS

A flashing red light is much more likely to draw our attention than a red light that is permanently on. In the same way, fleeting signals are effective because the audience doesn't get too familiar with them. And the more readily a signal can be turned on or off or varied, the more detailed the information it can convey.

Tyrant flycatchers (*Tyrannidae*) have reddish-orange or yellow crown feathers concealed on the top of their heads which are rapidly uncovered and erected to signal that a bird is likely to attack. The name tyrant reflects their pugnacity towards crows, hawks, and other large birds, which they harass with great determination. In the same way, the expandable brightly coloured dewlaps under the chin of the male Anolis lizard (*Anolis* spp) are normally collapsed and invisible, but when they want to threaten a rival or impress a female, these dewlaps are inflated.

Using striking visual signals can also be a good way of alerting others to danger. The black-and-white patterns on the rumps of most deer and a great many African antelopes become especially conspicuous when they sense danger. An individual may erect the hairs and lift the tail in the air, as white-tailed deer do, or swish the tail rapidly from side to side like Thomson's gazelles. Travelling in a vehicle in the Serengeti in Tanzania, you can see mixed herds of Thomson's and Grant's gazelles grazing in abundance, but as you approach closer some individuals look up and start swishing their black tails, creating a strobe effect across their rumps. When they turn away, the swishing tail clearly says, 'I'm out of here', a signal that is picked up by near neighbours and spreads like a shock wave through the whole herd in seconds. In order to get enough food a gazelle must spend most of the day with its head down grazing, so a highly conspicuous signal is vital and usefully shared between species. The gazelles may also send a message directly to the predator. For instance, if chased by a pack of wild dogs, while fleeing they do sudden vertical leaps called 'pronking' which tell the predator that they are strong and healthy and not about to be run down.

Another kind of 'flash pattern', most commonly found in birds, helps to keep the flock together. Many gregarious birds have contrasting patches of colour on their wings, tails or lower backs. These are normally hidden when a bird is perched or on the ground, but are suddenly revealed when it is about to take flight. The Canada goose has two separate patches which are used to say 'Ready, steady' and 'Go'. The first is a white area under its chin which contrasts with its black head and neck. This is visible all the

Like many plains antelope, impala are constantly at risk from predators, so they also have an eye-catching way of signalling danger to each other by rapidly swishing their tails back and forth across the vivid markings of their rumps.

time, but becomes much more so during the head-tossing display that indicates a bird is ready to move off. The family, however, will only take note if the head-tossing is performed by the gander who leads flights. Any tendency to impatience by immature individuals is thwarted because their white patch is marred by dark flecking. When the gander is poised to take flight he extends his wings and suddenly reveals another badge, the white patch at the upper base of his tail. This is the signal for the rest of the flock to follow.

Starlings, like many other birds, gather together in flocks – some of the largest are made up of millions of individuals. By roosting together the birds share each other's warmth at night and gain safety in numbers. But when coming in to roost, how do they co-ordinate their movements so perfectly, twisting and turning in unison so that they seen to be governed by a single will? Although it might appear to us to be the ultimate in crowd control, the way it is achieved is surprisingly simple, and in this case it is graphic designers and computer programmers, rather than biologists, who have come up with the answers. By creating a programme in which the behaviour of the birds is replicated by 'boids', and applying three simple rules, the boids can be made to flock like real birds. The first rule is separation: Don't hit other boids. The

second, alignment: Try to match your neighbour's speed and direction. And finally, cohesion: Try to keep close together. These basic rules are the same whether you are a bird, a fish or a human, and although they don't explain every aspect of the birds' movements, they do tell us how such perfect alignment and effortless synchrony is achieved.

Physiological changes can alter an animal's appearance very rapidly, as we know from the way we blush when embarrassed or turn pale when startled or frightened.

Physiological changes can alter an animal's appearance very rapidly, as we know from the way we blush when embarrassed or turn pale when startled or frightened. Many fish, including groupers, triggerfish, goatfish, and some species of wrasse, change colour even more frequently as a form of display. Teleost fish typically are light-coloured below and dark above to camouflage themselves by 'countershading' from the light from above, but the Asian teleost fish (*Badis badis*) can assume eleven different colour patterns in different circumstances, hence its common name, the Assam chameleon fish.

But the unrivalled kings of costume drama are giant cuttlefish (*Sepia apama*). The shallow waters of Spencer Gulf in southern Australia are distinctly cool for diving in May and June and I donned a thick wetsuit to gain some protection. As soon as I was

NEPTUNE II
OCEAN reef
NIRA
OCEAN reef

beneath the surface, however, I forgot about shivering and was transported into another world. Everywhere I looked, giant cuttlefish hovered like spacecraft among the seaweed, their thin filmy skirts rippling around torpedo-shaped bodies. Underneath veined white markings, soft pastel shades of green, red and blue wash across their skin, sometimes changing to become ghostly pale or darkening to rich burgundy and emerald. They change direction with as much ease as they change colour – gliding smoothly forward, backwards and sideways – or with a sudden spurt they can retreat or propel themselves headlong. The long arms or tentacles that extend from their large heads are also beautifully coloured and patterned with pale stripes, curling and extending like the arms of a ballerina. The males are larger than the females, growing up to about a metre over their three-year life span, their tentacles fringed with banner-like webs.

When I went to investigate one of them more closely, the cuttlefish watched me with its thin slit eye and then began a miraculous transformation, not only in colour but in texture and shape. It paled before my very eyes and little bumps and flaps appeared on its skin, growing increasingly prominent while its tentacles became gnarled and rigid, branching upwards. Within seconds the cuttlefish had taken on the appearance of the seaweed around it, camouflaged so perfectly that had I not been but a few feet away I would have never guessed it was there at all. As I backed away, its skin smoothed and gained colour and I watched it abruptly reappearing as a cuttlefish as if by magic.

Little is known about these cuttlefish. Most of their lives are spent out at sea unobserved, but in the early winter months of the southern hemisphere they gather in their thousands in Spencer Gulf to breed. Large males jealously guard their females, which hide among the vegetation and in rock crevices where they lay their eggs. If another male approaches too closely, the guarding male fans out his web-fringed tentacles like a banner and black zebra stripes pulse across the side facing his rival. If he feels seriously threatened he may tilt broadside to his rival, the stripes flashing across the expanse of his back. Sometimes both males will take up this pose and then real aggression may be called for. Darting

OPPOSITE | Swimming with giant cuttlefish in Spencer Gulf in South Australia where they come to breed.

forwards with their tentacles splayed out, they reveal a sharp beak with which they can easily tear off a chunk of flesh. All around, there are smaller satellite males hovering hopefully but, given the stiff competition, how can they ever hope to gain access to a female? The answer appears to be, by being exceedingly sneaky. They don't bother with impressive displays but impersonate females instead. Going pale and mottled, and tightly curling up their tentacles, they appear to fool the large males, slipping right past them to the females. When a large male is otherwise engaged dispensing with a rival, the 'transvestite' can suddenly reveal himself as male and grab the female. It *looks* as though he is trying to swallow her whole as he wraps his tentacles around her head and transfers sperm packets to a pouch below her beak. She then lays large eggs, one by one, which are fertilised as they pass over the sperm in her pouch and are attached to the underside of boulders or rock crevices. If the large male returns to find his female with a sneak, the smaller male can rapidly take on a female disguise again and avoid getting into trouble.

Although the whole communication system of cuttlefish and octopus seems to be based on visual signals, astonishingly, these creatures are colour blind. We know this firstly because their retina only has one visual pigment, which means that they are unlikely to be able to discriminate wavelength, and secondly because, during behavioural experiments, they were unable to distinguish between different colours. They have complex eyes and well-developed vision, but they can only see shades of black and white. For them, changes in brightness and texture of the skin are what is important. But what they lack in colour vision, they make up for in another channel of communication: they can detect plane-polarised light, which we humans cannot see. We know this because cephalopods can easily learn to attack (or not) a torch covered with a Polaroid sheet according to whether the plane of light is oriented vertically or horizontally. Sharks and dolphins, which are predators of these cuttlefish, cannot see this type of light either. It is suspected that cuttlefish use this channel of communication to send messages to each other while remaining camouflaged from their predators.

OPPOSITE ABOVE | Cuttlefish are masters of disguise taking on the appearance of their surroundings.

OPPOSITE BELOW | Male cuttlefish display at each other by tilting broadside with their tentacles spread out while black stripes strobe across their backs.

BODY LANGUAGE

A wolf pauses on a ridge top and stands briefly silhouetted against sweeping skies before it disappears down a steep bank and into shadow. Sheltered on the leeside of the hill the pack are taking a rest, some sleeping while others watch the pups at play. Grey or timber wolves (*Canis lupus*) live in packs of between seven and twenty individuals. At the heart of the pack are the alpha male and female, the only pair who will mate. Some individuals leave the pack as juveniles, but others stay on and help to raise the litter of pups produced by the alpha couple. Scent-marking, yips, barks, growls and the classic low mournful howls are all part of wolves' rich vocabulary and are used to define and defend territories (Chap 4, p.143 and Chap 2, p.60). But at close quarters, within the pack, family relationships are mediated by an extensive 'language' of body postures. A three-month-old pup lowers his head and front legs while sticking his bottom in the air, then suddenly jumps up and grabs another by the scruff of his neck; they tumble, chasing each other through the grass. Another pup stands stiff-legged and tries to exert authority over his younger brother by giving him a brisk sideways shove. A young adult joins the pack and rushes to the dominant female, nuzzling and touching his damp nose to hers. Only the wolves themselves and an informed observer can read the signs of submission in this friendly greeting. The new arrival's ears are held back and his tail is kept slightly lower than the alpha female's. All is well.

The bodies of animals, like our own, act like moving billboards advertising their intentions. Although the dominance hierarchy in wolf society is strict, it tends to be maintained rather casually and it is usually sufficient for the subordinate to give only a small gesture of submission such as lowering the tail. However, just as we square our shoulders or stand with arms akimbo to show confidence, if there is any dispute over the respective rank of two wolves, the dominant animal will stand tall and face his opponent. With hackles raised, tail bushy and held horizontal, ears erect and slightly forward, he may add a direct threat by drawing his upper lip back to expose powerful canines. In order to defuse the ten-

Body language is a very important means of communication in a wolf pack. Dominance is conveyed by standing tall, with tail and ears raised while a subordinate will lower its tail and puts its ears back.

sion, the subordinate may lower his tail between his legs and cower as he approaches, before rolling over to expose his belly. But if he thinks an attack is imminent he may take up a defensive stance, displaying a mixture of signals. His tail may be between his legs, his head low and ears flattened against his skull, but his mouth is open in a snarl, the hair on his neck erect and his body arched in anticipation of a fight.

As we have spent at least 14,000 (and the most recent evidence suggests as much as 135,000) years in the company of domesticated wolves, we are familiar with much of this body language. Our pet dogs communicate with us (as members of their pack) using the same signals as their wild relatives and we have learned some of their language, though we may interpret it in our own way. If you arrive home and your dog jumps up and licks your face, you probably regard this as a fond and exuberant greeting. In dog terms, it is certainly a welcome, but one with a slight difference. The dog is actually behaving in exactly the same way as a hungry wolf pup greeting an adult returning from a kill. By licking the adult's face, the pup is asking its older relative to regurgitate food for it. Holding out a paw for us to shake seems such a quaintly human gesture that we may think we have taught the dog a whole new language, but wolves also hold out their paws to each other, either to show submission or as an invitation to play. Play often involves the same kind of movements as an attack and so body language is especially important to show that intentions are friendly. Adopting a posture like the 'play bow', in which a pup crouches, head down, bottom in the air and tail wagging, is such an unambiguous signal that the pup can safely go on to nip its fellow without being regarded as aggressive.

Of all a dog's body language, the most conspicuous is the wagging of its tail. Tail up and wagging is a sign of friendliness, playfulness, anticipation and excitement; tail tucked under and wagging frantically means that the dog is nervous. We know that tail-wagging is purely social. Dogs will often wag their tails in anticipation when getting their dinner; however, video footage of dogs which had been observed to do this showed that they did not wag their tails when they received their food if there were no people present. Tails are such an important device for communicating that lots of members of the dog family – including many jackals, foxes, dingoes – have a black or white tip to their tail to make their movements more conspicuous, and the tail of the exceptionally social African wild dog has a highly visible black-and-white tip.

The tails of primates are essentially designed to give them balance when leaping through trees, but many species also use their tails to make a statement. The long, elegant tail of the ring-tailed lemur of Madagascar is smartly striped in black and white and its visibility enables the whole group to stick together in the forest. One of the most expressive tails I have ever encountered belongs to the recently discovered sun-tailed monkey (*Cercopithecus solatus*) which, as its name suggests, has a glowing goldy-orange tip. The tail of the dominant male is kept vertical at all times, the very tip flicking the air with savoir-faire as he leads his group through the tangled undergrowth of the West African rain forest. A perfect example of a useful appendage becoming a visual signal.

We all know that if you want to attract attention one of the best ways is to wave your arms above your head. We even employ this method to send quite complicated messages using semaphore code. And we are not alone. Fiddler crabs thrive in salt-water marshes around the world and by far the most striking things about them are their pincers. One is dainty and elegant, the other is a sharp-pointed, colossal appendage as big as the crab's entire body. Only the males are endowed with these massive claws, which are useless for feeding but which make powerful weapons and may be used to threaten other males. They are also used to attract the attention of females. When the tide is in, fiddler crabs live underwater in an elaborate labyrinth of tunnel-like burrows, often rolling up a ball of mud to plug themselves in with a pocket of air for breathing, but when the tide ebbs they scurry to the surface with sex on their mind, the males waving their claws above the mud flats in a desperate entreaty to females to 'come hither'. A team of biologists from the University of Witwatersrand in South Africa reports that several males will surround a female and begin to wave their claws in synchrony like 'a band of conductors trying to orchestrate the performance of a single player – the female crab in their midst'. It may be that the males' waving together allows females to make direct comparisons between the apparatus of each one and select the most impressive.

From a fiddler crab's perspective the enlarged claws of males must appear truly colossal.

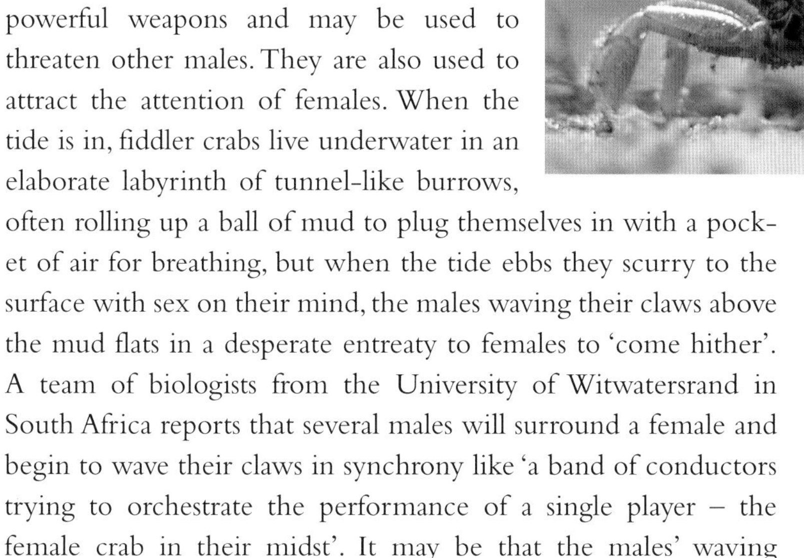

So important is this claw that in one species (*Uca annulipes*) males who have lost it cheat and rapidly grow a flimsy substitute of the same length. This is utterly useless as a weapon but works just as well when it comes to threatening rivals and waving to females. Each species apparently has its own choreography, which is rather lost on us as we tower above them. From the point of view of the crabs, who can see 360 degrees but only a thin slice of about two centimetres above the horizon, the waving displays must be powerful spectacles.

Understanding other animals' body language can sometimes be

imperative for survival. There are more than 375 varieties of shark in the world and none are great conversationalists. They have a highly tuned sense of smell and may also use their electrical senses to communicate, but they use body language too and divers ignore it at their peril. White-tipped reef sharks (*Triaeonodon obesus*), for instance, are highly territorial and do not take kindly to someone the size of a human hanging around in their patch. If approached by a diver, the shark may change his normal swimming pattern into a more exaggerated movement, his nose upwards, pectoral fins turned down and his body contorted into an S-shape. This change in posture is not an invitation to play – the shark has a short fuse and can move rapidly into a head-on attack, gaping mouth slashing from side to side as it hurtles through the water at its victim – a signal that no one would be hard-pressed to interpret! Mike de Gruy, an underwater film-maker, learned this the hard way. He was scuba-diving at 15 metres off the Marshall Islands in the Pacific Ocean photographing sharks, when he noticed a particularly strange-looking female grey reef shark. He thought she was injured, as her nose was up, her pectoral fins lowered, and her mouth slightly open. He decided to take her photo, but as soon as the flash fired, the shark broke out of the posture and came straight for him. She pushed the camera aside and grabbed his arm in her mouth, ripping off a sizeable chunk of flesh. Eleven-and-a-half operations later, Mike's arm is almost back to normal, but he now thinks twice about ignoring a shark's warning.

Male chimpanzees make themselves half as big again by raising the hair on their bodies.

Certain kinds of body language are almost universal among mammals and can be reduced to a few basic principles. To appear threatening, animals make themselves look as large as possible and present their weapons of war – teeth, tusks or horns. Likewise, submissive or unthreatening postures usually involve crouching, looking as small as possible and showing vulnerability, as when a dog rolls over to expose its belly. There are many equivalents in human body language. If threatened, we may draw ourselves up to our full height, square our shoulders and perhaps brandish a weapon in the face of our opponents, but we will crouch down to comfort an unhappy infant or submit at gunpoint by putting our hands in the air to indicate that we are not holding a weapon. One of the funniest stories I heard which neatly demonstrates the shared body language of humans and animals was at a zoo in Washington, DC. It was feeding time and two ostriches, impatient with waiting their turn, decided to steal food from the keeper's wheelbarrow, trying to intimidate him by approaching with their wings spread out to their full extent. However, they quickly retreated when the keeper, cognisant of intimidation tactics, turned on them and opened out his jacket wide!

Making yourself appear large and dangerous is actually a good way of avoiding real physical violence. Male gorillas stand upright and beat their chest with cupped hands. Male chimpanzees make themselves appear half as big again by raising the hair on their bodies and charging around, tearing at vegetation, brandishing branches, hurling rocks and slapping the ground. These displays are clearly meant to frighten bystanders, but it is very seldom that anyone gets hurt. Having said that, personal experience has taught me that being in the wrong place during a display can be dangerous. Branches or rocks have come flying my way and, worse, on one occasion I found myself actually incorporated into the display, being used instead of a branch and dragged along the ground by a very worked-up male!

Normally, however, subtle signals are sufficient to maintain the social order. The dominant, or alpha, male chimpanzee sometimes needs only to raise his hair slightly before low-ranking members of the community rush to appease him, crouching low and bobbing their heads up and down as though bowing, while giving low, breathy grunts. Another sign of submission is the reverse of 'presenting arms' and involves the subordinate crouching and turning his back towards the dominant individual. When performed by females this has the additional function of allowing the male to assess her reproductive state and is even used by females as a 'come on' if they want to mate. One day I was watching a young female called Flossi. At about nine years old, she had just hit puberty and was eager for sexual experience. And because she came from one of the most powerful families in the community, she wasn't bashful about making the first move. I watched in great amusement as

ABOVE TOP | A nervous chimpanzee reaches out and is reassured by a dominant individual.

BELOW | Holding out a hand palm-up is the way chimps beg for food or ask for reassurance.

OPPOSITE | An embrace is an important way of reaffirming solidarity between chimps, especially during tense situations.

she walked along a branch and presented her backside to a young male who was obviously a bit gauche. Undeterred, Flossi kept backing up into him, until he was positioned on the very end of the branch, at which point he had little choice but to comply with her demands!

Gestures add another dimension to body language and, like humans, chimpanzees make extensive use of their arms to convey different messages. A rapid dismissive sweep of the arm can be used to tell another to get lost, a dominant animal might reach out and touch a crouching subordinate to reassure it. These are both very reminiscent of human gestures, as is reaching towards another individual with palm up to beg. Sometimes infants will hold their outstretched hand right up against their mother's mouth in an attempt to get food and, during a tense situation, reaching out to a dominant animal can be an entreaty to be left alone or a plea for assistance during a fight.

FACIAL EXPRESSIONS

Most of the apparatus we use to sense the world around us – our eyes, nose, mouth and ears – is located in our heads and, at close quarters, the face itself can provide a great deal of information. Humans are estimated to have as many as 7,000 facial expressions to convey what they are feeling and the face and its role in communication has become a hot topic. But what are the origins of the smile or frown?

Bushbabies travel through the high branches of Africa's equatorial forests after dark. They forage alone but keep in touch using the plaintive baby-like calls which have earned them their name. They also scent-mark their aerial walkways with sticky urine

footprints, providing a catalogue of vital statistics on their sex, age and reproductive status. Given their lifestyle, it is easy to appreciate why sound and smell are good ways of sending messages, while visual signals, such as facial expressions, are of little use. However, observations of the Northern lesser bushbaby (*Galago senegalensis*) in captivity reveal that when a bushbaby meets up with another of its kind it will flatten its ears and partially close its eyes. If the animal is low-ranking it may do so from some distance away, while a high-ranking animal may come very close before it does the same. If especially eager to make contact, bushbabies adopt the same expression and in addition withdraw the corners of their mouths in a slight grin, emitting cries. Not much is known about the significance of this facial expression – which is the same whether the animal wants to groom, share food or attempt to mate – but as bushbabies live in the dark it seems unlikely that pulling faces at each other is an important means of communication. Instead it may simply be a throwback to a basic reflex.

Only one group of mammals, the primates, really use their faces to talk.

Facial expressions in both animals and humans often accompany vocalisations, but some of the earliest expressions may have originated from our natural reactions to startling or unpleasant experiences. Any extreme or sudden change in the environment may be a potential danger and a reflex to protect the major sense organs is a sensible precaution. This reflex is remarkably similar in most mammals, including man, and probably developed quite early on in mammalian evolution. When encountering a strong smell, an unpleasant taste, a sudden loud noise or even if anticipating a blow to the head, the response is more or less the same. The head is withdrawn, the eyes scrunched up and the eyebrows lowered to protect them. In many animals, the ears are also flattened against the head for protection (this is sometimes even detectable in humans), the lips drawn back and the corners of the mouth pulled wide. The function of this 'grin' may be to expel noxious substances from the mouth as the tongue is often protruded while grinning and the glottis closed. Another possibility is that the 'grin' exposes the teeth in readiness for attack.

In many mammals this basic protective response has become a more ritualised form of communication. For example lions, horses, wolves, foxes and dogs all exhibit a 'low grin' in social interactions, especially when greeting a superior or in slightly tense situations. But, for the most part, animals' facial expressions remain a limited and not very significant means of communicating. Only one group of mammals, the primates, really use their faces to talk. Primates often live in tight-knit groups with others in view most of the time. This sets the stage for close-up encounters where the face has become a vital source of information about the identity, emotions and inclinations of others. Jane Goodall, who has spent a lifetime closely observing chimpanzees, describes a scene in Gombe in Tanzania where a group of chimpanzees had just been provisioned with bananas. It may sound like a cliché, but the chimps absolutely love bananas, and squabbles over them can be quite intense. On this occasion there had obviously been enough to go round, or nearly. An infant male was eyeing a banana peel that lay discarded beside a sated adult. The infant approached very slowly. Then, carefully monitoring the adult's expression, he reached out extremely cautiously and picked up the banana peel. Only after the whole operation was successfully completed, which took several minutes, did he take his eyes off the adult's face.

A defensive reflex is seen among most mammals in anticipation of a sudden blow to the head where the ears are flat, eyes closed and mouth pulled back at the corners. This facial expression may have evolved into a more general form of greeting in animals like lions because it is clearly unthreatening.

Small monkeys such as marmosets and capuchins have the same kind of facial muscles as their larger relatives, but because it is difficult to see their little faces at any distance away, their use of facial expressions to communicate is quite limited. For larger monkeys, apes and man, the face is such an essential bulletin board for self-expression that they have lost the hair on their faces. In order to gauge just how important facial expressions are for social interaction among rhesus macaques (*Macaca mulatta*) a researcher carried out a very disturbing experiment. He removed various individuals from their social group, sectioned the eighth cranial nerve and then put them back with the others. Cutting the nerve completely

CLOCKWISE FROM TOP LEFT | Chimpanzees often spend time sitting and apparently contemplating life; a young chimpanzee pouts when distressed; a baboon gives a 'yawn threat' exposing his canines; geladas have taken some facial expressions to extremes – this 'lip-flick' is a threat; a 'fear grin', probably an exaggeration of a protective expression and likely to be the origin of our smile.

eliminated the animals' control over their facial expressions. The individuals concerned were still able to call and use body language, but the absence of facial expressions had a dramatic effect on their social relations. They interacted less, tended to drop in social rank and were involved in more fights. There was also a marked diminution in the bond between mothers and their infants.

Facial expressions are concentrated around the eyes and the mouth in primates because during their evolution there has been both increasing intricacy and control of muscles around the lips and eyes and a corresponding decrease around the ears. Flexible lips may have evolved for testing the ripeness of fruit and serve as almost as another hand when grooming.

The flexibility of primates' lips allows them to produce a wide range of expressions, some so exaggerated that they are quite comic. For all young chimpanzees, weaning is a traumatic time. When they are about five years old, their mother starts to prevent them from suckling and they whimper and pout, protruding their lips to form a trumpet. If their mother ignores them they become increasingly distressed and this pouting may alternate with a horizontal pout in which the mouth corners are drawn back wide but the lips still protruded in an expression very reminiscent of a Donald Duck cartoon. The whimpers escalate to high-pitched squeaks of frustration and perhaps even a full-blown screaming tantrum. These expressions so clearly convey the infant's distress that it is heart-rending to witness and it must take a very firm resolve on the part of their mothers to ignore it.

One of the most common expressions seen among primates is the 'fear grimace', or 'fear grin', in which the mouth is open and lips retracted. This is almost certainly an exaggeration of the protective response discussed earlier, given by animals who are tense or frightened to appease high-ranking or aggressive individuals. Such a clear, non-threatening signal is of enormous value to social animals who interact at close quarters, as there is not much leeway if you misjudge a situation. This may well be the origin of our smile; it is easy to see how an expression of appeasement could become a fast and effective way of sending friendly signals for a highly co-operative species.

A direct stare represents an aggressive threat in most primates. I was filming gelada baboons in Ethiopia a few years ago and wanted to get right in amongst a huge crowd of them without causing alarm. If I looked directly at the animals while approaching they would move off but by crouching low and shuffling backwards, pretending to be utterly absorbed in my shoelaces, I could get close to them. Staring might be found threatening because it is a very good indication of confidence and this is exaggerated by lowering and drawing the eyebrows together in a frown. However, among apes and humans staring is more complex. Among chimpanzees and bonobos staring can be a way of making positive contact and recent research on gorillas indicates that staring is used in a variety of contexts, including greeting and even appeasing older males. Whether aggressive or otherwise, in close-knit social groups the direction of gaze provides important information to others and may be the reason why we have kept prominent eyebrows.

LIGHT SHOWS

After dark each night, in the balmy air of Malaysia's coastal mangrove forests, thousands of tiny fairy lights wink and flash. So closely crowded are the minute beacons that whole bushes and trees appear to be pulsating with radiant light. The lights are in fact so bright that local fishermen several kilometres out to sea use them to navigate. The dramatic show is produced by male fireflies (*Pteroptyx tener*) flashing a 'Come and get me' message to the females.

Fireflies are in fact not flies at all, but beetles, and the light they emit is not fire, but bioluminescence, or 'living light', which is produced by a chemical version of our electric light. When we switch on a light, electrical energy is supplied to the metal filament in the bulb, which results in excitation of each atom's electrons. These then leap away from the nucleus and as they fall back towards it they radiate heat and light, giving us electric light. Fireflies don't use electricity. The basic process is similar but it is food rather than electricity that provides the energy, and instead of a metal filament the energy is directed at a group of proteins called luciferins, or 'light bearers'. Boosted by an enzyme which acts as a catalyst, this

Fireflies are really a kind of beetle and flash out messages rather like Morse code to attract females.

biochemical process is far more efficient than electricity and doesn't waste any energy as heat.

Each species of firefly flashes its own pattern of pulses, the males lighting up in unison to enhance the effect of the message and turn the heads of the females who fly overhead. But it is not only females who are attracted by the flashes of light – other males are, too, and they settle on the bushes with the most impressive constellation of lights. When new males first arrive, their flashing is unco-ordinated, but the newcomers' rhythm is soon brought into harmony with their neighbours', until there are literally thousands, all flashing simultaneously.

There are several theories about why male fireflies synchronise their flashes, but the most likely is that females appear to prefer males with the earliest, brightest flashes. The males can't flash too early because, just as in Morse code, keeping the right gaps between flashes is critical, but each male tries to be the first to give the following flash, with the result that soon there is less than a split second difference between them. This effect, called 'entrainment', keeps everyone flashing in perfect time. When a female chooses to alight on a particularly bright tree, the group of males around her change to a different, more subtle phase of signalling and she starts to respond. Not much is known about this intimate dialogue, but if the pattern of pulses exchanged is correct, a male will approach the female and mate.

Other fireflies attempt to attract their partners on the wing. In these cases population densities are often low and solitary males cruise around, emitting the signal that is unique to their species. The females respond with their own pattern of flashes. As a male and female continue to signal in turn, he can home in on her and mate. Receptive females are so taken by these eye-catching exchanges that they don't play hard to get but respond eagerly to all patrolling males. Other luminescent females go further and are actually the ones to make the first move. The wingless female of the common glow-worm (*Lampyris noctiluca*) found in Britain gets impatient waiting around for a male to come and court her and has found a simple but effective way of advertising her eagerness to mate. She climbs to the top of a grass stem or twig and waves a glowing bottom towards the sky, a technique that is sure to stop any passing male in his tracks!

As I emerged from the water, the tiny creatures that still clung to me continued to emit light so that sparkling silver sequins spilled from my arms and hair.

We are basically land animals who spend most of our time in daylight, so we tend not to appreciate just how many marine animals produce light of their own. One of my most memorable experiences was swimming at night on the island of Vieques, just off the coast of Puerto Rico. As my arms parted the dark waters they produced a ripple of shimmering lights spinning all around me so that I felt as if I was floating through a galaxy of stars – as it was above, so it was below. These magical lights are generated by millions of tiny marine plankton called dinoflagellates, but the individual lights can be so intense that they appear simply as an aura around your body. I have been told that when it rains, each drop that touches the water creates a spot of light until the whole bay is suffused in a bluish-green glow. As I emerged from the water, the tiny creatures that still clung to me continued to emit light so that sparkling silver sequins spilled from my arms and hair and it seemed as though I was stepping out of a fairyland.

It may have seemed like a wonderland to me but this is a serious business for the dinoflagellates. They produce light in reaction to the movement of the water, which acts as a burglar alarm. When the water is disturbed by a grazing predator such as a copepod (the burglar) these tiny creatures flash a bright light. This attracts a secondary predator such as a small fish or squid (the police), which is more likely to eat the larger copepod than to bother with the minuscule dinoflagellate. It is a great way of diverting attention away from number one, and other marine animals have adopted a similar protection policy.

Ostracods are small crustaceans which have been nicknamed 'fireflies of the sea' because, like fireflies, they make extensive use of sophisticated light signals. They use light as a means of protection in a similar fashion to the dinoflagellates. They have many enemies and when attacked by cardinal fish, swimming crabs, shrimps or anemones, they can produce a brilliant and massive bomb cloud of light which not only attracts bigger predators such as snappers and jacks but also temporarily blinds their enemies. It can so startle them that if they have already swallowed an ostracod they are liable to regurgitate it in surprise! However, ostracods rarely need to use this trick, as most predators seem to know that they are booby-trapped and give them a wide berth.

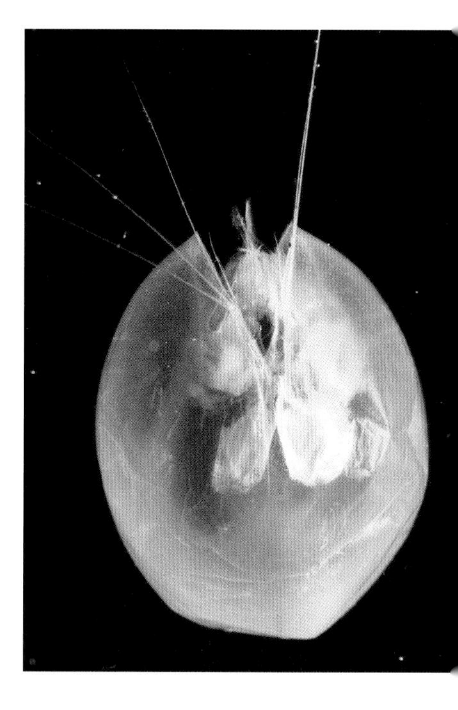

Deep sea ostracods send messages by leaving glowing trails of light in the water.

For an hour or so at the end of twilight the ostracods perform their amazing light shows, leaving no one in much doubt about their identity. Each species has a unique display. The males paint distinctive patterns of bright blue light in the water to attract females. Unlike fireflies, they produce the light outside their bodies by secreting into the sea a cocktail of chemicals from separate sets of tiny nozzles on their upper lips. These chemicals then mix and react with oxygen in the water, creating a trail of glowing bubbles. The males swim very fast, the equivalent of someone of our size crossing one-and-a-half football pitches in a single second, and as they go they squirt their coded pattern of luminescence in their wakes. For some species, these trails of light are only a few centimetres long but for others they may be several metres; some move downwards, others upwards, some laterally and still others obliquely, like a child tracing pretty patterns with a sparkler.

We are only just beginning to decode the ostracods' messages. Jim Morin of Cornell University is the world expert and describes how the pattern starts with long-lasting pulses of several seconds.

At first the tiny orbs of light are widely spaced but they get progressively shorter and closer together until finally short, evenly spaced pulses die out into the darkness. The initial part of the display is the main spectacle for many ostracods, but a few concentrate on a grand finale of short, emphatic, evenly spaced pulses. The light show is an invitation to the females, who spend most of their time close to the seabed, to come up and party. Although the female does not appear to send any kind of acknowledgement in return, by cueing on the right location, trajectory and light pattern, she can presumably track a male of her own species and mate with him. Other males are also drawn to the lights and escort the main performer through the water, but for reasons that have yet to be explained these escort males, although equally capable of pulsing, remain 'silent'. Sometimes trails that are widely spaced start to synchronise (probably due to the same phenomenon of entrainment exhibited by fireflies) and produce a breathtaking natural spectacle of blue incandescence sweeping the length of the reef.

What is it about light that fascinates us so? From the glowing aurora of polar skies to dramatic flashes of lightning, the twinkling lights of Christmas decorations to the spinning laser beams of a rave, there is something about light which we find both mesmerising and magical. Early studies of marine animals from the deep tended to bring the animals up to the surface, which usually destroyed their delicate light-emitting structures and left us completely ignorant of the sheer numbers of animals that are capable of producing light. In fact the most abundant vertebrate on earth is a little bioluminescent fish called the benttooth bristlemouth (*Cyclothone acclinidens*). By mounting cameras in ROVs (Remotely Operated Vehicles) which can see into the ocean's depths we have discovered an extraordinary world of sparkling lights, glowing trails, spinning halos and luminous lipstick. Among the most spectacular of these creatures are medusae, which have a central disc in which light races round and round so that it looks like a spinning Catherine wheel of the deep sea. We now know that 80 per cent of marine creatures emit light in order to find mates, avoid predators, lure food and stick together, but we are only just beginning to decipher the meaning of their flashing codes which may prove far more complex than we have ever imagined.

One of the most intriguing light sources is found in flashlight fish (family Anomalopidae), a widespread but primitive creature with a blunt snout, large upturned mouth and a curved light organ under each eye. In this case the light is not produced by the flashlight fish itself but is in fact a lush growth of luminous bacteria. These produce a lime-green glow that is then enhanced by silvery crystals inside the organ, acting like a mirror. Whether the bacteria get anything other than a free home is not certain, but the fish definitely benefit from their live-in torches. The light is generated continuously and the fish control the signal by closing flaps of skin or, in some species, rotating the whole organ round to face the other way. They use the lights to attract prey and to communicate with each other in order to form schools and sexual bonds but also as a way to misinform predators. If one

ABOVE | The illumination of a flashlight fish is produced by a growth of bioluminescent bacteria below the eye which act like a natural torch.

BELOW | To turn off the light the fish closes a flap of skin – or in some species rotates the bacteria to face the other way.

Lantern fish have light organs on their bodies that they use to communicate not only with other lantern fish but also with different species.

When lantern fish encounter tuna, the males turn their lights to full beam, grabbing the attention of the predator while the females make good their escape in darkness.

approaches, the flashlight fish blinks and rushes to escape, swimming away rapidly with its lights on full beam. As the predator chases after it, it quickly covers the lights and, under the mask of darkness, sneakily swims away in the opposite direction! Given that each fish can do this up to seventy-five times a minute and they do so in large groups, it's no wonder the predators become completely confused.

So many marine creatures are light-sensitive that it is not surprising that light is used not just to communicate within a species but between different species. Some, like the flashlight fish, use light as a burglar alarm or to confuse predators; others use it to lure predators in. Lantern fish (family Myctophidae) turn themselves into martyrs and send out beacons of light that spell their doom. In some species, only the males possess light organs, or at least large ones, which are positioned on their tails and capable of producing bright, rapid flashes of light. Tuna are one of the lantern fishes' main predators, but examination of the stomach contents of tuna hauled up by fishermen has shown that the lantern fish they eat are predominantly male. Why should the females escape from the tuna when both sexes are readily caught in the fishing nets dragging the same area? The reason appears to be that when lantern fish encounter tuna, the males make the ultimate sacrifice for their females. They turn their lights to full beam, grabbing the attention of the predator while the females make good their escape in darkness.

Lantern fish aren't the only ones who make sacrifices for their females. In the depths of the oceans lurks the rather sinister anglerfish (order Lophiiformes). Dangling in front of its mouth is a tantalising light that glows in the inky-black water. Like wreckers luring ships on to the rocks with their lanterns, this fish lures its prey into its jaws. This fatal attraction also plays a part in sex. Different anglerfish have very different-looking lures and it was once thought that these attracted different kinds of prey. However, since the fish are solitary, it is hard for males and females to find each other and it is now believed that the lures are also a sexual signal that attracts the much smaller males to the right kind of female. On finding her, though, his fate is unenviable. He latches on to the skin of his chosen female with pincer-like teeth and her

A deep sea anglerfish uses its luminescent lure to attract prey and also to attract females.

bloodstream steadily grows into his body until he becomes no more than an appendage, a little sack of sperm waiting to fertilise her eggs when the time is right.

DANCE AND DISPLAY

On the vast savannah of equatorial and southern Africa a bird rises like a phoenix above the golden grass, its long tail streaming out behind it. In wide open spaces you can be seen from a long way off and male widow birds are not at all shy about drawing attention to themselves. The females are inconspicuous, but the males in breeding dress are among the most handsome of all seed-eating birds. Paradise widow birds (*Steganura paradisea*), jet black with fiery gold-and-red chest and a long black tail, are a striking sight against the open horizon. Rising up 50–100 metres they perform spectacular courtship displays, hovering, flapping their wings and waving their tails in an attempt to entrance the females.

An elaborate exchange of signals, repeated over and over again, acts as a kind of engagement ceremony during which the pair form a close bond.

Such an extravagant, eye-catching display is bound to get the widow bird noticed by the female – but also by every other animal in the vicinity, including predators, so why does he jeopardise his safety? It may be that this is in itself part of the attraction for the female; it is a display that says, 'I am so fit and strong that, despite this tail, I can fly and escape if need be, so choose me!'

Finding a mate and reproducing are an essential part of all animals' lives. Females are often choosy about the father of their offspring, so it is frequently up to males to prove themselves, either against rival males, or by appealing directly to the female through a courtship display. However, courtship displays are not exclusively performed by males. For animals that form faithful couples, an elaborate exchange of signals, repeated over and over again, acts as a kind of engagement ceremony during which the pair form a close bond.

Many birds are monogamous and both parents remain together to raise the chicks. An especially charming ritual is performed by blue-footed boobies (*Sula nebouxii*) in the Gulf of California and the Galapagos. The booby's name may come from the Spanish 'bobo', which means clown, and here is the reason. When courting, the male makes full use of his large bright blue feet. First he parades around his territory, advertising himself by stretching out his wings and pointing his beak straight up to the sky. If this 'skypointing' gets the female's attention, he faces her and then slowly raises each of his bright blue feet in succession, turning them outwards in an arc. If she likes his footwork, she responds by raising hers. Now the couple take it in turns to skypoint, and then hold their bills up while looking away from each other before lowering their bills on to their chests in the 'shy-looking pelican' posture. Finally they again wave their comic feet at each other.

As part of his courtship ritual a male blue-footed booby points his beak to the sky, while showing off his bright blue feet to the female.

The routine is repeated several times over, while the male whistles and the female honks, until gradually their movements become synchronised. After mating, the couple perform another ritual, nest-building, during which each bird will pick up stones and twigs, show them to his or her mate, and then place them carefully where they have been displaying. Boobies actually like to lay their eggs on bare ground, so the nest serves no practical purpose at all. As soon as the female is ready to lay her clutch of eggs the nest is scraped away, removing every twig and stone to clear the area again. The exercise is purely symbolic, an important ritual element in the pair's bonding with each other.

Far out in the great blue expanse of the oceans it seems that the whole business of reproducing might be a bit hit and miss. Pelagic fish are extremely difficult to study, so our knowledge of their behaviour is very limited, but it seems that on the whole they don't bother to form couples or defend nesting territories. Instead there are mass spawnings where trillions of gametes are released into the water, triggered by the very rapid swimming of the shoal.

In contrast, many coastal and freshwater fish take a little more time and trouble over the process of mating. They swim to the bottom, stake out territories, prepare a nest and then perform elaborate displays in order to attract a partner. The problem is, it is usually the males who claim the territory, sometimes make a nest, and are so geared up to be protective of the brood that they are even inclined to attack approaching females. The importance of the courtship dance is to soothe the male and develop mutual trust. A female taking up an invitation from a male teleost fish had better beware. He will usually attack her as soon as she enters his burrow. To appease him, she remains almost motionless and gently leans against him with tautly spread median fins. Then, gradually, the couple start a carousel, butting against each other until at last they reach the point of enfoldment. The fish wrap around each other, the female pulsating while she ovulates and finally, as the pair disengage, the eggs rain down into the nest.

Seahorses are very faithful to their partners and an elaborate greeting ceremony is performed every day to strengthen the bond.

Long-term fidelity is rare in the fish world. Seahorses are a notable exception. They and their cousins, which include pipefish (family Syngnathidae), are found in tropical and temperate coastal waters all round the world. I had my first encounter with a seahorse when diving in the Red Sea. They are perfectly camouflaged and move very slowly, relying on ambush to catch their prey of small crustaceans. I had all but given up hope of finding one when a tiny movement in the seagrass caught my eye. Fixing my eyes religiously on the spot, I swam over to find a delicate green-coloured seahorse about 15 cm long. Their strange but elegant appearance with long tubular snouts, body armour and prehensile tails makes them immediately special, but most fascinating is their exceptional method of reproduction: with seahorses, it is the male who gets pregnant.

White's seahorse (*Hippocampus whitei*) is an Australian species about 10 cm long and the first to have been properly studied in the wild. Both sexes have their own home ground – the males can have a patch as small as a single square metre, while the female's area may be a hundred times the size. Seahorses find a partner and remain paired throughout the breeding season and their devotion to each other is reiterated daily.

Every day after dawn, they perform an elaborate greeting ceremony. The male goes to their usual meeting point and waits for the female. At the sight of each other they literally 'light up', brightening from a dark brown or grey to a pale yellow or off-white. Then they take their place side by side and with their tails they grasp a shoot of the seagrass, and begin to circle around it, the male taking the outside. Periodically they let go of the shoot and swim slowly across the seabed, parallel to each other and perfectly synchronised, the male grasping the female's tail with his as if holding hands. After a minute or two they return to circling the maypole. After about five minutes of circling and parallel swimming, one of them, usually the female, darkens and moves away. Sometimes the male will pursue her and try and persuade her to continue, in which case she may concede and dance with him a little while longer before swimming off and going about her own business.

Seahorses won't even abandon a partner that is injured and unable to reproduce.

When seahorses are ready to mate they have a very prolonged greeting ceremony. The male pumps the water around him with rapid side-to-side body movements while the female 'points', raising her head. She then inserts her ovipositor into the brood pouch on the male's tail and transfers her eggs. He will now care for the developing embryos, aerating and nourishing them for several weeks before releasing the independent young. Greetings between the pair continue throughout pregnancy and appear to co-ordinate the reproductive states of the male and female. When the male releases his brood, the female appears with her eggs hydrated in readiness for fertilisation and the pair usually re-mate within a day.

The greeting ceremony does more than keep the pair in touch with each other's reproductive state. It creates an absolutely steadfast bond between them. If a single seahorse greets a paired seahorse, the latter will simply ignore any overtures and only the death or disappearance of one of the pair can break up the 'marriage' during the breeding season. Seahorses won't even abandon a partner that is injured and unable to reproduce. In one study a paired male was unable to brood because of an injury to his brood pouch, but his partner continued to greet him. She didn't hydrate any eggs, or mate or display with any male for nearly two months. When her mate finally recovered, the pair re-mated within a week. In another case, a female tried to greet her mate, who was very badly injured, without getting any response at all for five days before finally abandoning her attempts. He subsequently died and only then did she look for another mate.

ARCHITECTS AND ARTISTS

Finding the right site and building a good nest is a measure of a bird's fitness and often used in courtship. The form of the nest has to be appropriate for rearing young chicks, but a little self-expression can also be effective for gaining an edge and winning a mate.

The hammerkop (*Scorpus umbretta*) is a strange-looking brown bird with a crest on the back of its head which mirrors its stout beak – hence its name, which means 'hammerhead' in Afrikaans. It lives around shallow lakes and swamps in central and southern Africa, southern Arabia and northern Madagascar, feeding on frogs, fish and invertebrates. In many places hammerkops are regarded with a great deal of superstition, frequently seen as evil omens or as the 'lightning bird', harbinger of heavy rains and storms. This may be because they seem to anticipate bad weather and move to drier areas, but probably the main reason they attract so much attention in local lore is their extraordinary nest. They can take around two months to build these huge domed structures of reeds, grass, dead plant stems, mud and dung.

The hammerkops start by building a sturdy platform nearly a metre (three feet) across in the fork of a tree. Over the next few weeks they bring more and more nest-building material, arranging it with the greatest of care until they have created a huge wicker basket. Both birds build the nest, but one of them, probably the female, has the last word if there is any dispute. Legend has it that other birds bring sticks as a contribution to the palace but the truth is that they actually steal from the structure to make their own nests. After about three months the roof has been put on and the nest is finally finished. It may comprise three separate compartments and overall can be almost two metres high, weigh some 50 kg and be strong enough for a man to jump on. The entrance is reduced in size with a mud portal and the nest lined with water weed and dry grass. Stones, snakeskins, animal bones, hoof and horns, porcupine quills and wildebeest flywhisk tails are found to adorn the roof. It has been calculated that by the time the final touches have been added each bird has flown some 480 km, half of that distance carrying a heavy load. Frequently the nest is used only for one brood, so why do they put such enormous effort into creating their lavish palace? The answer is, no one really knows. Certainly it is virtually impenetrable to predators, but it seems to go far beyond what is required for hatching and rearing their young. It may be quite simply that the joint effort of building the nest creates a very strong bond between the pair. Only when it is complete will they mate.

The hammerkop not only builds a palatial nest but also decorates the top with snakeskins, feathers, bones and horns, which has inspired local legends about its magical powers.

During courtship they hop on and off each other's backs, balancing precariously on their spindly legs for a minute or so while flapping their wings and squawking loudly. True mating follows, using similar displays, and then the clutch (usually three to seven eggs) is incubated for a month. Close co-operation between the pair is required as the young are highly dependent and need their parents' care for another three months or so. The nests are also settings for group ceremonies when as many as ten birds may gather, calling loudly while running around each other in circles, crests raised and wings fluttering. No one really knows what these are all about and it may just be their way of letting off steam in tense or unusual situations.

Some birds don't build nests to attract a mate but still take a lot of time and trouble to create the right setting for their courtship.

A female satin bowerbird sits in a bower of twigs constructed by the male while he offers her a bouquet of leaves.

Various species of birds are meticulous in clearing an area for their displays, much as we might use a podium or stage to enhance a theatrical performance. The real prize for stage building and set design goes to the bowerbirds of Australasia.

The satin bowerbird (*Ptilinorhynchus violaceus*) is always on the lookout for some pretty new trinket to adorn his stage. Male bowerbirds build amazing structures of twigs and decorate them with ornaments found in the forest. I was deeply impressed by the first bower I saw. A very neat avenue of twigs sat in the middle of an area of about a square metre which was laid with dry grass, meticulously tidy and free of dead leaves. A veritable art collection was carefully arranged on the front porch – iridescent blue feathers, small pale blue flowers (blue is a favourite colour), shiny insect exoskeletons and a couple of rounded yellow leaves. Around the perimeter lay a neat row of white snail shells. Not long after we were settled under the trees, the owner himself returned with a series of churring sounds: a stout, midnight-blue bird who regarded us with piercing blue eyes as he hopped down from a branch to his bower. In his beak he triumphantly held a blue pen which he put in pride of place at the entrance of his bower and then flew off. A few minutes later he was back and this time got down to work painting the walls of twigs with pine which he mashed up gently in his beak and applied carefully by running his beak up the length of each twig. Apparently the first thing a female bowerbird would do on arriving is inspect his paintwork. No one knows exactly why painting is important but it is possible that by tasting the pine walls the female bird gleans valuable information from the male's saliva about the state of his health.

However well kept the bower, his possessions and paintwork are not sufficient to convince her to mate. After inspecting the paint she settles in the bower while the male begins to dance. Spreading his wings and fanning out his tail he hops about his stage among the trinkets, giving a range of churring and rasping calls and intermittently making a series of delightful sounds borrowed from other birds in the forest such as whistling kites and brown falcons. The male bowerbird can quickly get quite worked up and the female, who likes a good show but doesn't like him to get over-excited, immediately adjusts her postures to calm or encourage him.

I was deeply impressed by the first bower I saw. A veritable art collection was carefully arranged on the front porch.

Many unusual research tools have increased our knowledge about the subtleties of animal communication but few have been as original as that used by Gerald Borgia and Gail Patricelli from the University of Maryland. They have built a very lifelike robotic satin bowerbird female, which can be made to move its head, open its wings or crouch down in order to find out exactly how the male's behaviour is modified by the female's body language. On one occasion when the male bird had gone on an excursion we placed the female robot in his bower. Gail gave me a quick lesson on impersonating a female bowerbird and then left me with the remote control, saying over her shoulder as she went, 'Good luck – remember to think sexy.'

To be honest, I didn't think it was going to work but when the male bowerbird returned he seemed delighted to have a female waiting for him. Using the remote control I turned her head towards him, making subtle adjustments to her posture so that she appeared to be alive. He deposited another yellow leaf by the bower and frantically removed a few dead ones. Then with a volley of hissing and chattering calls he went into display mode, dancing before her in an enchanting fashion. I made her crouch and he got increasingly worked up. When I brought her upright again he cooled off a bit. When I lowered her back into a crouch position, which is apparently a very definite sign of encouragement, he needed no further persuasion and jumped on to the robot to mate. It felt quite strange to be communicating with a bird like one of his own kind and, though it was very rewarding in a way, I couldn't help but feel a bit guilty for fooling him. At least it was all good practice for the bowerbird. The better a male is at reading a female's body language, the more successful he will be, and the rewards are great – a male can pair with as many as thirty females in a season. But however good his dancing, if his bower is not up to scratch the female will look elsewhere.

Building constructions is not limited to birds – some of the greatest architects are insects.

Bowerbirds are some of nature's most enthusiastic designers. The very grandest bowers are built by the Vogelkop bowerbird (*Amblyornis inornatus*) from New Guinea. In some areas the male of this species builds a huge, open-fronted, roofed hut up to 2.2 metres tall and two or more metres across. Below the bower he plants a lawn of soft green moss which sets off the piles of colourful objects he carefully positions on top. These are replaced as soon as they fade. The real nest is built by the female after she has been mated by her chosen male; she incubates the eggs and raises the young on her own while the male stays with his bower to try and attract more females.

Building constructions is not limited to birds – some of the greatest architects are insects. Two species of solitary hunting wasps use architectural design to pass messages between generations. After mating, the females of *Rygchium foraminatum* and *Trypoxylon clavatum* construct a chain of little brood cells consisting of hollow twigs with cross-walls of mortar in which to leave their eggs. The female wasp will die after laying her eggs but along with each egg, she leaves supplies – enough paralysed prey to nourish the hatching larvae into adulthood. There is only one exit to the 'burrow' and the young wasps will emerge in reverse order of age: the last egg to be laid is nearest the exit and its pupa will leave first, the next youngest will emerge second, and so on. At first the larvae

The sumptuous bower of the Vogelkop bowerbird is surrounded by carefully arranged objects which are replaced as soon as they fade.

can move around in their cells while feeding but after the pupal state, when they are ready to metamorphose into mature wasps, the cells are generally too small for them to turn around in. If at this stage they are oriented the wrong way, towards the blind end of the burrow, there are serious consequences. Not only are they likely to get trapped and die; it will also result in the death of their older siblings. So the larvae have to get into the right position before entering the pupal state, but within the confines of their cells how can they possibly know of the location of the exit? The answer is that they must rely on signs left by their mother. When she made the burrow she made the exit walls distinctively rough and asymmetric, thereby leaving a message that her offspring receive only after her death.

4

Chemical Communication

Pheromones can be very powerful. From an array of carefully labelled bottles and vials worthy of any alchemist, Steve Alm, from the University of Rhode Island, selected a tiny glass vial and handed it to me. He warned me that I need use only a drop and so I cautiously tipped a tiny bit of the clear liquid on to my finger. The effect was miraculous. Within minutes the air was speckled with dark dots as hundreds and hundreds of oriental beetles appeared over the horizon, flying low over the grass and making straight towards me. Steve had created an exact chemical copy of the female beetles' sex pheromone which had a compelling effect on the behaviour of males.

OPPOSITE | The queen honeybee in her chamber attended by her workers. The queen's pheromones regulate the behaviour of the whole colony.

PHEROMONES ARE CHEMICAL signals, widespread among insects, that elicit a stereotyped and often dramatic response. Among mammals, odours tend to have a more subtle effect, acting as 'primers', but can be potent none the less. Chemical communication is primeval. It goes far back to the dawn of life. Single-celled creatures evolved to respond to subtle chemical changes in their environment, including the changes associated with approaching predators, prey or mates. Their microscopic bodies were equipped to read chemical signals accurately, but not patterns of light or sound. In fact, the majority of animals on the planet still communicate mostly or entirely with chemicals.

Chemical communication is primeval. It goes back to the dawn of life.

There are several advantages to using chemicals to communicate. Molecules can be light and carry on the wind over huge distances. Chemical compounds can also be highly concentrated and influence the behaviour of thousands of individuals almost simultaneously. And, under the right conditions, some compounds are stable and so unlike calls or visual signals that chemical messages can last for weeks, months and, as we will discover, even generations. They are especially useful for animals who are very widely dispersed because they can be left like a calling card and picked up later. However, the downside of chemicals is that they cannot be addressed to a particular individual and can therefore be picked up by anyone.

SEXUAL SIGNALS

Polar bears are usually solitary and can roam more than a thousand kilometres a year across the sculpted ice floes of the Arctic. Given these vast distances and the fact that females breed no more than once every three years, male polar bears have their work cut out to find a mate. The only way bears can communicate effectively over such a huge range is by leaving scent messages for each other. If a male comes across the smell of a receptive female he is instantly besotted – males have been known to follow a female's tracks for over a hundred kilometres in a straight line across solid pack ice. Some potent chemical signal from her urine or from secretions in the soles of her feet must tell the male that it is worth the effort because he resolutely ignores the tracks of other bears that

A male polar bear can roam over 100 km across the pack ice following the scent of a female.

criss-cross his path. When he finally catches up with her, she may have as many as five or six other males already in tow and so he has to fight for her attention. Because of the females' long breeding cycle, adult males effectively outnumber available females by three to one and competition is fierce. Male polar bears can weigh more than 650 kg and the fights can be dramatic. As is so often the case in nature, the largest male usually wins.

Sexual scent messages are widespread among animals and may be produced either by males or females. Chemical compounds may be emitted from glands which have specially evolved to serve a communicative function or are simply passed out when urinating. There are great differences in animals' sensitivity to smells.

Flicking out its tongue a Burmese python picks up chemical information about a potential mate or its surroundings.

Olfactory receptors are located on a group of scroll-like bones in the nose called 'endoturbinales'. The surface area of the endoturbinales gives us an approximate idea of the number of receptors and so the degree of sensitivity. In an Alsatian dog this is about 200 square centimetres (sq. cm) while in humans it is only 4–5 sq. cm. Some animals also possess an additional sensory organ called a Jacobson's organ. If you see a snake flicking its tongue in and out in an inquiring manner, it is picking up chemical information about its surroundings, or about potential mates, and transferring this information via a series of ducts to this special organ in its mouth. Many marsupials and ungulates also have a Jacobson's organ. For example, on discovering a female's urine, male black-tailed deer (*Odocoileus hemionus*) both sniff it and lick it. Then they perform a distinctive 'Flehmen response', curling back their upper lip, opening their jaws and shaking their head to transfer the smell to the Jacobson's organ in the roof of their mouths in order to obtain more detailed information about the female deer's sexual condition.

Smell is unique among communication systems in that it directly informs animals about what is going on in each other's bodies. And because odours are linked to hormonal changes they often serve as potent sexual signals. Indeed, there is such a thing as chemistry between people. A partner's scent – not what he or she splashes on, but a personal, unadulterated odour – can be recognisable and appealing to a lover. But how much of a hidden chemical dialogue passes between us without our even being aware of it? Experiments have shown that men have a preference for the odour of T-shirts worn by women when they are ovulating over the odour when they are not. None the less, given that smell is so blatantly important in the sexual encounters of many animals, why is it so discreet in humans? The answer might be because it is advantageous for human females to keep males guessing. The argument goes that if females are too obvious about when they are receptive, males may not stick around to help them raise offspring when they aren't.

Black-tailed deer curl back their upper lip in a 'Flehmen response' to pick up smells and then by shaking their head they transfer the information to the Jacobson's organ in the roof of their mouth.

We may gain more insight into our own behaviour by studying the use of smell in primates. The forest-dwelling marmosets of South America are among the smallest of the group, measuring no more than 90 cm, of which about a third is tail. For a long time it was believed that the females of these appealing little creatures practised what is called concealed ovulation, so that the males did not know when their fertile period was. This would mean that although a pair could mate at any point in the female's cycle, the male needed to stay in constant attendance in case anyone else impregnated her and passed on his own genes, instead of those of the first male. This coyness is in sharp contrast to the swollen pink bottoms and blatantly provocative behaviour exhibited by female great apes and Old World monkeys such as baboons, and is a clever way for the female marmoset, who tends to need help raising her young, to keep the father of her children around.

But recent studies have suggested that although the female

marmoset shows no great change in her behaviour at the time of ovulation, her sexual chemistry is enough to alert the male to her condition. When levels of luteinising hormone (which stimulates ovulation) peak in the female pygmy marmoset (*Cebuella pygmaea*), the behaviour of the male undergoes significant changes. As one might expect, he becomes much more interested in the female, sniffing her, attempting to mount her and showing other signs of arousal. Obviously she uses a much more subtle form of communication than her larger African cousins – so subtle that her mate still needs to stay around and protect her from the attentions of any other roving male.

For insects, chemicals act as 'releasers' and have a direct and compelling effect on the recipient.

Mammals are such complex creatures with large, complicated brains that it is often quite difficult to analyse their use of chemical signals. Although they may respond to smells, they may also react to sight and sound at the same time, adding the various signals together in order to interpret their message. For insects, though, chemicals act as 'releasers' and have a direct and compelling effect on the recipient.

Female silk moths (*Bombyx mori*) produce a sexual attractant called bombykol, to which males are highly sensitive. Just a single molecule is enough to trigger a nerve impulse in a receptor cell of a male, and only a few hundred molecules – which is a minute proportion of the bombykol released by the female – may be enough to have him heading off to find her. Because of this extraordinary sensitivity, the pheromone can be effective over distances of up to 48 km; released into the wind it forms a long, invisible plume leading to the female.

Insect pheromones are being studied intensively and the reason is primarily economic. Insect pests are responsible for literally billions of dollars' worth of damage to crops every year but the use of conventional insecticides has incalculable effects on the balance of nature and the environment. So, controlling insect populations with pheromones which can draw them into a trap or specifically inhibit a particular insect's reproduction is highly desirable.

The worst offenders among the crop-eaters are caterpillars of all kinds, so many of the studies have concentrated on butterflies

Male danaid butterflies collect poisonous compounds from a heliotrope plant which they convert into alkaloids. Females are attracted to males bearing the poison because it can be passed on during mating and incorporated into the eggs as a protection against attackers.

and moths. As a result, we have some fascinating glimpses into the private lives of Lepidoptera. Many butterflies also use chemical signals to attract a mate, but members of the danaid group have a particular refinement that enables the females to choose the male who will be the best father for her children. Male danaids have two brush-like structures known as hairpencils tucked into their abdomen. When they are courting a female, these hairpencils emerge and stroke her antennae with their bristles. This may seem like nothing more than a friendly gesture, designed to check out whether the female is receptive or not, but in fact the hairpencils are transferring a substance known as danaidone to the female. Experiments have shown that the more danaidone the male has on his bristles, the more likely the female is to accept him as a mate.

Danaidone is closely related to poisonous compounds called pyrrolizidine alkaloids which are found in some flowering plants. Most insects give these plants a wide berth, but not male danaids.

They actively seek out and feed on such plants and then convert the alkaloids in their bodies to danaidone. But why should females be attracted to males with these poisons? The reason is that danaidone can be passed on to them during mating and incorporated into their eggs to protect them. Potential attackers detect the presence of a toxic substance and steer clear. So the females know that a male who has plenty of danaidone on his hairpencils will give her offspring the best chance of survival.

In the early years of studying sex pheromones, scientists assumed that each animal emitted its own unique mix of chemicals, in order to attract only mates of its own species. We now know that this is not the case, and that a number of closely related species produce pheromones that are indistinguishable from each other. So how does a gypsy moth (*Lymantria dispar*), for example, know that it shouldn't mate with a nun moth (*L. monacha*)? Part of the answer appears to lie in such a surprisingly simple device as timing. In Europe, where both species are native, the gypsy moth is diurnal, normally mating any time between 9 a.m. and 3 p.m. The nun moth doesn't start its mating flight until 6 p.m., so the chances are that they won't overlap.

Further analysis of the components of sex pheromones has led scientists to believe that butterflies and moths – and probably many other creatures as well – use laboratory precision in detecting the exact chemical composition of the alluring substance. Two tortricid moths, the cabbage leafroller (*Clepsis spectrana*) and the summer fruit tortrix (*Adoxophyes orana*), inhabit the same areas and seem to mate at the same time of day. The females secrete and the males respond to the same pheromone, which has two known chemical components. The key lies in the ratio of one of these substances to the other. The summer fruit tortrix prefers more of one, while the leafroller prefers more of the other. Similar experiments with more complex sex pheromones have produced similar results.

Sex pheromones are much more than mere 'Come hither' signals. To begin courtship, the male tsetse fly (*Glossina morsitans*) literally puts out feelers, touching the female with his tarsus. What initially arouses him is simply the movement of another fly, but this in itself gives him no clues as to whether the object of his attention is female. A receptive female accepts his advances by secreting what is known as a courtship pheromone, while if the male accidentally approaches another male, he is instantly warned that he is wasting his time by a 'Don't touch me' pheromone.

Pheromones can also be a general invitation; bark beetles use pheromones to summon others of their kind to a potential breeding site. They are tiny creatures that breed by boring into suitable trees and excavating galleries in which the females lay their eggs. Again, the chemical signals are sophisticated and highly specific to each species. Some species are attracted to healthy trees, some to unhealthy ones and others to newly felled timber; some prefer the crowns of trees, others choose different parts of the trunk. So a number of species can feed on the same tree without anyone getting in anyone else's way.

If the male tsetse fly accidentally approaches another male, he is instantly warned that he is wasting his time by a 'Don't touch me' pheromone.

Beetles that breed in dying trees may be lured to them by the ethanol released as the wood begins to decompose; in other instances, they seem to pick a tree at random, do a test bore and if necessary move on until they find a suitable host. In any case, once an individual has decided on a promising tree, it emits a chemical signal to summon others of its kind to what is called a mass attack. Beetles pour out of nowhere on to the tree, all emitting the same 'aggregation pheromone', until the tree is literally saturated with them. In some species, once a sufficiently high concentration of chemical is reached, the pheromone is even able to announce that the tree is full. Arriving beetles get the message, land on a nearby tree and continue the assault there.

However, while it is part of the definition of a pheromone that it passes information on to members of the same species, in the case of bark beetles the chemicals can be interpreted by other species too. In California, two species of bark beetle, *Ips paraconfusus* and *I. pini*, both feed on the ponderosa pine tree and both do less well if they try to infest the same tree. To avoid this, the aggregation pheromone of one species actively repels members of the other species, sending the message 'We were here first – get off'. However, some larger species of beetle can also read the aggregation pheromone and find it very enticing. Like catching the smell of dinner, the pheromone allows them to home in on a site where they can expect to find plenty of bark beetles to eat. Presumably the bark beetles find safety in numbers and enough of them survive such an attack for a healthy population to continue.

CHEMICAL CONTESTS

Unlike visual signals or vocalisations, chemicals can be unpleasant, even harmful to the recipient, and can send a message that is as direct as a punch in the face. Some animals clearly say 'Go away' by simply releasing a pungent smell. This is particularly common in minks, polecats and badgers but reaches its zenith in the striped skunk (*Mephitis mephitis*).

An alarmed skunk raises its tail and ejects a jet of noxious musk at an aggressor.

Very few animals have the power that the skunk has to eject a jet of acrid liquid into the face of an aggressor. The liquid, known as musk, is a sulphurous compound, detectable to the human senses at a concentration of as little as ten parts per billion, the equivalent of one teaspoon per 1.3 million gallons of water. The skunk's anal sacs contain about 15 millilitres of this noxious deterrent. Entry to the sacs is controlled by a sphincter muscle similar to the one that regulates the flow of urine in humans. An alarmed skunk simply arches its back, raises its hindquarters and tail, relaxes the sphincters and sprays away, covering a distance of four to five metres. It can repeat the action six times in quick succession, and will then take four to six days to replenish its supply. However, like many acts of aggression in the wild, this is a last resort – it is always better to persuade a predator not to attack than actually to do battle. Although it is strikingly striped in black and white, the skunk is primarily nocturnal and spends much of its time in dense vegetation, so visual signals are not much use to it. Instead, it will stamp its feet, click its teeth and hiss as an audible warning to its antagonist before going into action. This behaviour may also benefit the predator, who doesn't waste any more time on noxious prey. It is interesting to note that the skunk is fastidious about keeping its own fur out of the way of its spray – apparently it, too, finds the smell distasteful!

No such delicacy disturbs the stink wars of the ring-tailed lemur (*Lemur catta*) of Madagascar. Looking a bit like a cross between a cat and a monkey, the ring-tailed lemur uses its long fluffy tail for balance as it sits on a branch or leaps from tree to tree. But this magnificent appendage, which usually has thirteen black-and-white rings, also has a more aggressive purpose.

Ring-tailed lemurs live in small mixed troops of which the leader is a dominant female. The males maintain the group's territory with scent-marking and a plaintive-sounding but penetrating call that can be heard up to a kilometre away. Females scent-mark more during the breeding season, advertising their status to the males. And it is then that the beautiful ringed tail comes into its own, as the males compete for the attention of females. Unlike other lemurs, ring-tails have scent glands on their wrists and under their arms, and a male rubs his tail against these glands, smothering it with a pungent secretion. He then waves the stinking tail above the head of a rival in an attempt to intimidate him. The other male responds in kind and sooner or later the smellier tail wins and the overwhelmed contender backs off. These stink wars help to establish dominance without anyone actually having to fight and risk getting hurt. Strong smells such as the lemur's stink armoury tend to be ethereal, while less intense smells are usually more stable and can last for long periods of time.

All sorts of animals defend themselves by producing toxins and alarm signals. The common earthworm (*Lumbricus terrestris*) secretes mucus from all over its body, to enable it to work its way easily through the soil. When it is stressed – by the presence of a predator, for example – it secretes much more mucus and adds an alarm pheromone which predators and other earthworms find repugnant. So not only is it fending off attack, it is warning others of its kind that there is danger about. In the same way, an aphid under attack from a predator may release a chemical warning which causes other aphids to drop off the plant they are feeding on and flee. Some social insects such as bees and ants, of which we shall hear more later in this chapter, may initially respond to an intruder by withdrawing into their hive or nest. Then, in a chemical change that is not yet clearly understood, they switch from retreat to attack. These alarm pheromones are lightweight, highly volatile chemicals which spread rapidly through a colony,

triggering the alarm response, and then disperse equally rapidly once the danger is past, allowing the insects to resume their normal activities.

Sea anemones are animals related to jellyfish though they look more like colourful undersea flowers. One of the most beautiful, as its name suggests, is *Anthopleura elegantissima* which lives in the intertidal regions of the coast of California. It measures about two centimetres across, and consists of a cylindrical column whose base is anchored to a rock and whose top comprises a mouth surrounded by tentacles. The mouth is the sort of glowing white normally seen in toothpaste commercials, while the darker tentacles are tipped with pure candy pink. The purpose of the tentacles is to wave about in search of food, which they then force into the mouth. But the waving tentacles are vulnerable to predators. When they are bitten, the anemone reacts with a quick convulsive movement, withdraws its tentacles into its mouth and remains tightly shut until no longer under threat. It also produces an alarm pheromone called anthopleurine to warn neighbouring members of its species that there is a predator about.

Sea anemones collect food with their tentacles but while waving them about they are vulnerable to predators such as sea slugs. This aggregating anemone not only produces an alarm pheromone to warn others that there is a slug about, but as the slug ingests the pheromone it carries a warning with it wherever it goes.

OPPOSITE | A male ring-tailed lemur combs his scent into his tail which he then waves about during stink fights with other males.

But the seas in which this particular anemone lives tend to be turbulent, and the movement of the water quickly disperses the anthopleurine, making the signal useless to all but the nearest neighbours. The communication system needs to be cleverer than that. The anemone's principal predator is a marine slug, *Aeolidia papillosa*, which, as it happens, does not easily metabolise anthopleurine. After nibbling at an anemone's tentacle, it stores the chemical warning in its tissues for the next five days, slowly releasing it into the water wherever it goes. So the predator itself is carrying the signal that alerts its prey to the presence of danger!

TERRITORIAL MARKINGS

Beyond the town of Palm Springs in southern California and its manicured golf courses and gardens, stretch hundreds of

Desert iguanas have a calm disposition – except during the mating season.

kilometres of dusty brown, sun-baked scrubland. The landscape appears to be empty until your eye catches sight of an elegant lizard, pale-speckled with a delicate crest running from crown to tail, sunning itself on a boulder, a desert iguana (*Dipsosaurus dorsalis*). As relaxed as they look, male desert iguanas are territorial during the mating and post-mating period of April to July and must assert their claim to a patch of land.

On the underside of each thigh, desert iguanas have a neat row of femoral pores which leave a twin trail of scent as they travel over rocks and dirt. This is an efficient way for a small animal to lay claim to a large area of land but there is a problem. In the low desert of southern California, where it is a blistering 45°C and bone dry, potent, highly volatile smells would evaporate in seconds, so iguanas use subtle, stable odours. They also protect their scent marks with a waxy coating that keeps them fresh for days. Even so, one would think that small patches of faint smell would easily be missed by fellow iguanas as they scuttle across the desert.

Intrigued by the problem of how the iguanas find the scent

marks Allison Alberts from the University of California, San Diego, undertook a little detective work and analysed the chemicals to discover their properties. What she found was that some components of the scent marks reflect ultraviolet light and so she started to investigate the iguana's vision. It transpires that iguanas have much better colour vision than we do and can also see ultraviolet light. Moreover, they have the lowest known threshold for discriminating differences in the level of reflected light from objects in their environment. Sand is one of the most reflective surfaces, so that to the iguanas everything stands out in intense contrast to the background. In this bright universe, their favourite food, the tiny yellow bloom of the creosote bushes, must glow to them like the neon signs of a roadside restaurant. Alberts thinks that, to the lizards, the scent marks might be extremely colourful – startling purple against brilliant yellow, for example – and all other iguanas have to do is approach and investigate. Once on top of the scent mark, they flick out their tongues and use their excellent senses of taste and smell to decipher the contents of the message. Research is still in progress but early results suggest that iguanas can tell the identity of the caller in their territory, whether male or female, neighbour, relative or stranger, and probably ascertain their breeding condition too. Generally tolerant of neighbours, relatives and potential mates, the desert iguana's usually calm disposition changes rapidly if a rival or stranger is trespassing.

Many animals make use of scent to mark the boundaries of their patch. Almost all terrestrial carnivores indulge in some form of scent-marking. Tigers are solitary and territorial and both male and female spray landmarks such as fallen trees or bushes to prevent conflicts. They tend to mark more heavily at boundaries, crossroads and other points where their claim to an area might be contentious. A tiger finding another's scent mark at any such point is likely to overmark it, asserting his (or her) claim over that of the neighbour's. The substance they spray is not urine but a white fatty 'marking fluid' which smells of ammonia. Both sexes may also raise their hind leg in order to direct the spray to a height of one metre or more above the ground. Rubbing landmarks with their anal glands and leaving visible scrapes in the ground, impregnated

OVER PAGE | Desert iguanas have special ultraviolet vision that means the scent trails they leave on rocks glow like beacons – as shown by this graphic representation.

Tigers leave scent marks at territorial boundaries or crossroads which other tigers may overmark to assert their claim to the area.

with scent from glands between the toes, further reinforce the message that this territory is spoken for. In the dry season scents can linger for weeks, but after the monsoons, tigers have to busy themselves re-signposting their territories because all the scent marks have been washed away.

When a female tiger is about to come into oestrus, she spray-marks more frequently than usual, alerting the male whose territory overlaps hers. In response to these signals the male also spray-marks judiciously – intensifying his 'keep out' message to other males and seeking out the female in order to mate – one of the few times that adult tigers willingly spend time together.

Most male members of the dog family mark their territories

just as the domestic dog does – by cocking a leg so that the urine is sprayed somewhere above ground level. One study of grey wolves showed that males did this on average every 450 metres, but much more frequently on the outskirts of their territory. Nearly half the markings were at the junctions of paths – making the signal as conspicuous as possible. And, the study noted, the rate of marking did not increase with a larger pack, suggesting that the marking was not done by all the males but was the privilege of the dominant member of the pack.

SIGNPOSTING THE ENVIRONMENT

Animals that are not especially territorial still leave scent messages for each other. Galagos, or bushbabies, are exclusively nocturnal and mostly forest-dwelling. They leave a scented reminder of their presence by rubbing chemicals from special glands on their chest and genitals along the branches of their aerial walkways and by peeing into cupped hands and rubbing the urine on to their feet (incidentally, the urine also improves their grip). Given that galagos probably have regular routes through the branches, these footprints must be as noticeable as the markings along a road.

Male galagos use urine to scent-mark more frequently than females, suggesting that they may be more possessive about their range; but it is not the only thing they are possessive about. When a female is in oestrus a male may pee directly on to her, or rub his chest against her to leave his scent on her and claim her as his own.

A Demidoff's bushbaby leaves a trail of scented footprints through the branches by rubbing its urine into its feet.

Many animals use the features of their environment to ensure that scent marks are picked up by others, whether the natural paths made by branches or a landmark bush or rock at the edge of a territory, but the position of the scent mark can also be highly informative. Male lions and cheetahs spray special chemicals from anal glands just below their tails to mark bushes and trees around their territories. They do this at conspicuous points and intersections in the same way as wolves and other animals do, but members of the cat family also draw themselves up to their full height and spray upwards, which could well be a clever tactic to make themselves appear as large as

The higher this dwarf mongoose can leave its mark the more conspicuous it is – and it might just fool others into thinking it's bigger than it actually is.

possible. Making a mark high up can be quite awkward for small animals but a few, such as dwarf mongooses, have hit on a great trick of doing a handstand in front of a vertical marker and rubbing their anal gland down it.

Leaving a mark is a good way to remember a particular place. Foxes, coyotes and wolves use token urination as reminders to themselves of places where they have foraged, scavenged or dug up food they had previously stored away. A urine mark may also remind them that, although the area looks promising and smells of food, it has recently been exploited and may not be worth lingering over. Studies of mongoose behaviour suggest that they, too, use scent-marking for this sort of 'book-keeping'.

The European otter (*Lutra lutra*) deposits faeces known as 'spraints' in prominent positions on rocks and tussocks. In some parts of its range, such as the Shetland Islands and areas of northern Scotland, it forages exclusively in the sea, but still needs fresh water to drink and to wash salt from its fur. Here, piles of spraint are distributed regularly along the coast, often built up into highly visible signals by generation upon generation of otters, so that an individual returning to land is never far from a spraint station. One spraint station then leads to another, steering the otter inland through the vegetation to a reliable source of fresh water. This benevolent behaviour helps not only the individual but other members of his species who may land on an unfamiliar stretch of coastline and be in need of guidance.

Brown hyenas (*Hyaena brunnea*) in the Kalahari Desert of southern Africa have an anal pouch from which they secrete a paste which conveys a double message. The pouch is normally tucked away inside the hyena's body, but in order to secrete its paste the hyena walks over a grass stem, bending it forward between its hind legs. It then curls its tail up out of the way, bends its hind legs slightly and extrudes the pouch, which has a long groove running through the central area. The hyena carefully positions itself so that the grass stem fits into the groove, which is covered with a white pasty secretion. It then moves forward, smearing the grass with a blob of white paste. As it continues to move forward and retracts the pouch, it releases a more liquid black secretion from glands located on either side of the groove. This has the effect of painting a thin smear of black just above the white paste on each stem.

Otters deposit piles of faeces, called spraints, on prominent landmarks over several generations. One spraint station leads to another and serves as a guide to fresh water.

Observers believe that the white paste, whose odour lingers for several weeks, is a territorial signal, designed to inform outsiders that this area is spoken for. The scent of the watery black secretion, on the other hand, lasts only a matter of hours and is more likely to tell members of the hyena's own pack that it has been foraging in the area recently and they should not waste their time here looking for food.

Brown hyenas are the only species to produce the black secretion, but all other hyenas paste in a similar way. In the confines of the Ngorongoro Crater in Tanzania, where a small area can support a clan of between 30 and 80 individuals, spotted hyenas (*Crocuta crocuta*) also tend to mark territorial boundaries and the area around a kill; in the much more open expanses of the Kalahari, where a group of nine may have to range over an area of 300 sq. km in order to find enough food, both they and the brown hyenas paste more in the centre of their territory than on the boundaries. Presumably a small group cannot afford to waste resources attempting to defend a large territory, so they concentrate on the core area where they spend most of their time and where food sources are most abundant. It is here and at the borders of the territory that they place their latrines – all members of the clan defecate in the same strategic places, building up a series of markers full of chemical messages. In the Kalahari, three-quarters of these are placed by shepherd's trees (*Boscia albitrunca*), a conspicuous landmark in this desert terrain.

OPPOSITE | A brown hyena investigates a two part message. The first, a white paste clearly visible here, says the territory belongs to his pack, the second, a watery black secretion, says that a member of the pack has been foraging here recently, so there is no point in wasting time looking for food in the vicinity.

Badgers have taken scent-marking to an even more complicated level. The Eurasian badger (*Meles meles*) is unusual among its family (which also includes weasels, stoats, otters and skunks) in that it lives in small clans consisting of several adults of both sexes, and their young. Although all badgers scent-mark using secretions from their anal glands, only the Eurasian badger has a large subcaudal (undertail) sac which contains and emits a complex cocktail of chemicals.

Eurasian badgers occupy a territory that may vary in size from about 15 to almost 200 hectares, although anything larger than one square kilometre (100 hectares) is unusual. The centre of the territory is a burrow known as a sett, which consists of a number

of individual burrows linked by tunnels. Throughout the territory, badgers dig communal latrines into which they defecate, urinate and deposit secretions from their anal glands and subcaudal pouch. The highest concentration of frequently used latrines is around the boundary of the territory; what is more unusual is that they are also found in close proximity to the sett.

This has led most observers to deduce that the outer circle of latrines is intended to mark the territory, and specifically to keep intruding males away from the clan females. Within that circle, the positioning of latrines is such that an intruder is more likely to encounter one the closer he gets to the sett – by which time he will be in no doubt that he is trespassing, and will have a fair idea of the size of the clan and the age and sex of its members.

Both males and females use the boundary latrines more often in autumn, probably because this is a time when the badgers are foraging far and wide, laying up stores of fat for the winter. All of this suggests that the scent-marking is not only designed to protect food sources but also to defend members of one clan from incursions from outside.

SOCIAL ODOURS

I was once greeted by a hand-reared wolf called Dakota who nuzzled and rubbed against me as I crouched down beside her. I was honoured – she was making me a member of her pack by exchanging smells. The smell of every individual is a complex blend of chemicals which differ in some way from those of other individuals, even if they are members of the same species. An analysis of beaver (*Castor canadensis*) scent, for instance, showed that it contains as many as fifty different chemicals which vary in concentration from individual to individual.

Meetings between lions and other members of the cat family begin with mutual sniffing of noses, with head and neck outstretched in curiosity. They often proceed to sniff and touch each other's nape, flanks and rear lightly with their whiskers. In friendly situations, cats often raise their tails to allow inspection from the other animals, but if uneasy, a cat will keep its tail down and step to one side so that individuals might end up circling each other trying to get whiffs of information. Scent not only identifies individuals, it can also provide information about an animal's social status and which group or colony it belongs to. Among lions who live in close-knit prides, body contact is a very important way of exchanging scents and reinforcing bonds between individuals. Female members of a lion pride – who are all related – greet one another with a special ritual which begins with sniffing noses, then rubbing heads and cheeks together and often brushing up

Lionesses greet by rubbing heads and brushing against each other in order to exchange smells and reinforce bonds between members of a pride.

against each other's sides. These actions are very similar to the sinuous contact indulged in by mating pairs, but they are in fact a practical way of communicating scent signals so that individuals are able to recognise members of their own group and identify potentially hostile strangers.

Mingling individual odours is a common way in which groups of mammals maintain a sense of solidarity. I have seen banded mongooses (*Mungos mungo*) go into a complete frenzy of sniffing and marking, winding themselves into writhing, squirming balls in the most enthusiastic of greetings when they have been separated for some time. Like other members of the mongoose family, they are highly gregarious animals which live in territorial

There is total solidarity in a banded mongoose pack.

packs of sometimes as many as 70 adults. Typically there are three or four breeding pairs in the pack and dominance somehow inhibits reproduction in low-ranking adults, but all members of the pack have very close relationships and present a united front when threatened by predators or other mongoose packs.

To keep group cohesion, they frequently rub and roll in the whitish musk which they deposit around dens and water-holes to anoint themselves with their pack's odour, and mutual marking is feverish after any period of separation. Carrying the scent of the pack is especially important when they are about to wage war against a neighbouring clan. Like wearing team colours in a football match, in the heat of battle it's an easy way of telling who is on their side. The bonds between members of a mongoose pack are so close that not only do they work together to see off rivals and mob any creature that poses a threat but will even rescue members of the pack who have been captured by predators. There is an amazing account of an alpha male climbing a tree where a martial eagle had landed with one of the adult males of the pack. The alpha male attacked the eagle with such ferocity that the eagle dropped its prey and the two made good their escape.

In certain species a group odour is achieved not just by rubbing and mingling each other's scents but by one or two individuals anointing other members of the group. The domestic rabbit is a gregarious species. As rabbits are mainly nocturnal and spend much time underground, they rely heavily on odours to regulate most aspects of their social life. This revolves around the warren. The colonies are divided into social groups which may contain anything from two to eight adults. Every group member has a clear position in the hierarchy which determines access to food, shelter and, in the case of males, to breeding females. Dominant females gain preferential access to the best breeding sites. All males help to defend the territory but the area is drenched in the dominant male's smell. He will also scent-mark other rabbits in the group by smearing them with secretions from his submandibular (under-chin) gland – or simply by spraying the hapless subordinate with his urine.

Among badgers, too, members of the same clan scent-mark each other to reinforce their relationships. They do this by means of a movement known as 'squat-marking', whereby one badger rubs its anal glands over another's flanks and rump, transferring traces of urine and other chemicals. The dominant male regularly squat-marks all the other members of the clan, partly to remind them who is boss, but also so that any squat-marking done around the outskirts of the territory bears his distinctive scent. Mothers mark their own cubs, making a stranger aware that the cubs have a powerful female looking out for their interests.

Males also mark oestrus females, an act which seems to make the female more responsive to the male's advances. And both males and females mark other females, perhaps as a way of maintaining the dominance hierarchy within the clan. The upshot of all this marking is that each member of a clan bears an identifiable mixed scent in which the alpha male's predominates. If two members of

Badgers have a clearly defined hierarchy within their clans.

a group meet at night away from their den, they check each other out by sniffing flanks and rumps – the areas most likely to identify an individual as friend or foe.

Scent-marking of individuals within a badger clan can also help to orchestrate the behaviour of its members. For example, it is often used as a means of appeasement when there is conflict. Adult males of many species frequently fight and inflict severe wounds, but this is inefficient behaviour for a hunter in the wild. Using sophisticated signals to assess a rival's strength and, if necessary, to back off means that a less powerful individual will live to fight – and mate – another day.

CHEMICAL COLONIES

The behaviour of many social animals is mediated by chemical messages but nowhere in the animal kingdom is social life so strictly under chemical control as it is in the world of insects. How can a single individual exert precise control over the behaviour of a crowd of thousands? The queen honeybee does just that as she sits securely in her chamber at the centre of the hive. She rules her colony by producing a special pheromone which is carried throughout her dominion by the ever-changing rota of workers who visit her. As long as the queen is in her parlour, and this fact is constantly confirmed to the rest of the hive, all is well – the workers keep working and the colony runs smoothly. But if anything happens to the queen, or if the colony gets too big or too crowded for the queen pheromone to reach all its members, chaos quickly ensues. The workers are no longer stimulated to forage, store food, build combs, or carry out any of the other tasks that keep the beehive ticking over. If the worker bees don't receive enough queen pheromone, they are able to concentrate on only one task: producing a new queen. So by secreting plenty of pheromone the queen is also securing her own position – no rivals will emerge as long as her chemical signals are strong enough to keep her courtiers happy.

But sooner or later the queen becomes too old to carry on, and her pheromone secretions weaken. As this stage, the workers may produce a number of 'virgin queens' as possible substitutes, and these contenders fight to the death to decide who is going to take over. As they do so, they eject a faecal fluid that repels the worker bees, keeping them out of harm's way until the battle is over.

Honeybees use pheromones to control every aspect of their complex lives. Even a dead honeybee makes use of chemical signals. The decaying corpse starts to secrete oleic acid, a fatty acid which stimulates live workers to remove the remains. Each bee carries the body only a few steps nearer to the entrance, but as every passing worker notes the presence of the acid and responds accordingly, the corpse inches its way towards the door, where it is finally ejected by the 'undertaker' bees.

The queen honeybee rules her colony by producing a special pheromone which is carried through her domain by the workers.

In times of crisis, honeybees produce a highly volatile alarm substance, isoamyl acetate, which alerts other members of the hive to the danger. In Japan this has developed into an interesting example of chemical warfare between two species of social insects. In autumn, a colony of the Japanese giant hornet (*Vespa mandarinia japonica*) may have hundreds of young in its nest that need feeding. One of its favoured prey species is the Japanese honeybee (*Apis cerana japonica*) and although the hornet is normally a solitary hunter, if it has made two or three successful forays into a honeybee hive, it marks the site with a pheromone to alert other hornets to the presence of food. If more than three hornets are attracted to the same nest they go into slaughter mode and can kill hundreds of bees in a matter of minutes. A group of 20 to 30 hornets can wipe out an entire colony in three hours, occupy the hive and carry the bee larvae home to feed hungry hornet mouths.

When a foraging hornet enters the hive the bees produce their alarm pheromone, quickly gathering reinforcements, and the hornet finds itself ambushed by angry honeybees. The bees form a seething, buzzing ball around the hornet, the temperature of which quickly reaches 47°C – fatal to the hornet, but not to the bees. The hornet does not live to mark the hive and attract other hornets, so the honeybees have staved off the mass attack that would almost certainly overwhelm them.

Ants use chemical signals just as much as bees do and, because they spend more of their time on the ground, they have added another signal to their repertoire: the trail pheromone. An ant travelling between its nest and a plentiful food source some distance away deposits tiny quantities of pheromone along the trail, leaving the unmistakable signal: 'Food'. Although there is no directional information in the pheromone, passing ants presumably know where their nest is and deduce that going the other way will lead them to a meal.

Trail pheromones pose a bit of a problem for the ants because, unlike alarm signals, they need to be reasonably long-lasting but not to direct the competition to a good source of food. The solution is to make the pheromone as chemically complicated as possible, so that other species cannot decipher the coded message. This trick doesn't always work, however. The wood ant (*Lasius fuliginosis*) is regularly ambushed along its food trail by a beetle, *Amphotis marginata*, which has learned to recognise the chemical signal for what it is. It has also learned that the ant, used to communal living, will regurgitate food to share with other members of its colony if it is tapped on the mouth. So the beetle taps, the ant regurgitates and the beetle feeds. If the ant counter-attacks, the beetle crouches down very close to the ground so that the ant can reach only its impenetrable outer casing. Abandoning this losing battle, the ant continues on its way, leaving the beetle to lie in wait for its next free meal.

African weaver ants (*Oecophylla longinoda*) – so called because they build nests in trees by fixing the leaves together – seem to use a combination of the trail pheromone, the alarm pheromone and a communicative dance to convey information to each other. As with most ant societies, the workers, who are all non-reproductive females, have clearly defined roles. Some are primarily foragers, while others stay at home to guard the nest and raise the larvae. But the discovery of a particularly rich food source means that the foraging workers need to recruit the nest-based workers to help carry food. In order to do this, the foragers leave a trail pheromone between nest and food source, but they also tell their sisters that something important is happening by performing a sort of waggling dance, touching the other ants with their antennae to

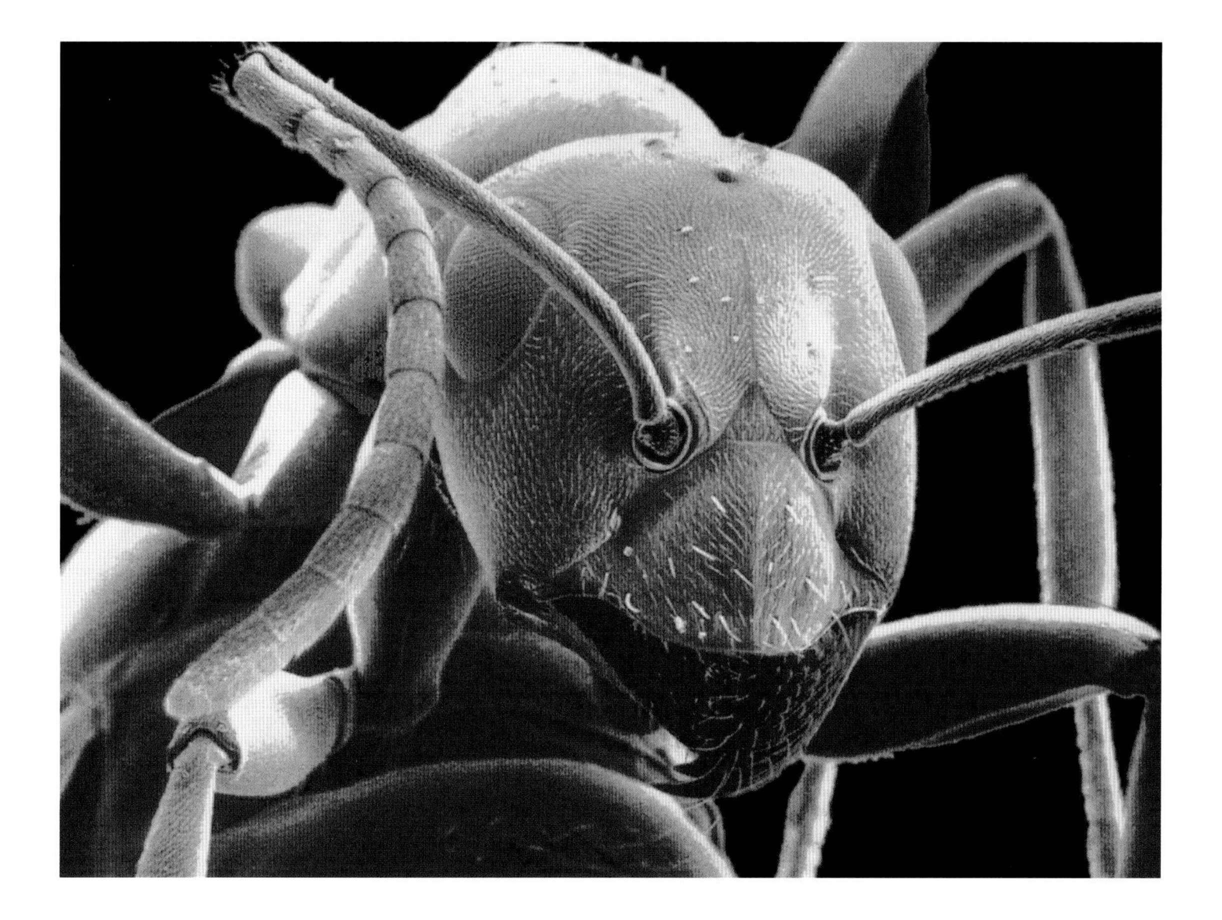

A wood ant produces complex chemicals to convey information about food sources.

communicate the odour of food. This is enough to stimulate nest-based workers to come and help stock the communal larder.

A foraging ant will stop looking for food in order to fight any intruder, even if the encounter is at an apparently safe distance from the nest. As she fights, she exudes alarm pheromones. If the intruders constitute a serious threat, some of the ants will leave the fight and race home to summon reinforcements, leaving a chemical trail behind them.

Back at the nest, the ants again perform their dance in front of their sisters, touching them with their antennae, but this time transferring alarm pheromone. Donald Griffin, in his book *Animal Thinking*, observes that the two dances, although similar, are not identical, so the combination of visual and chemical signals tells the nest-based ants what the crisis is. Griffin also remarks that after the 'Come and fight' dance, not all the ants depart immediately;

An African weaver ant persuades a fellow worker to feed it by tapping a particular spot on its mandible.

some repeat the 'recruiting' gestures to others in the nest. This is a most unusual example of an animal passing on information about a situation it has not encountered directly, a sort of Chinese whisper working its way through the ant colony.

John Bradshaw, a British entomologist, discovered another alarm system in African weaver ants, this time based on multiple pheromones with different meanings. When a worker meets an enemy in her colony's territory she releases a mixture of four chemicals from large glands in the head which open to the outside at the base of the mandibles. The individual chemicals diffuse at different rates through the air so that the other workers receive the different ingredients of the cocktail at different stages. The first is an aldehyde called hexanal and is the lightest. This prompts the sister ants to pay attention. The second chemical is an alcohol, hexanol, which causes the ants to search for the source of the problem. The third is undecanone, which attracts workers to the site of the trespasser and stimulates them to bite any foreign object they encounter. Finally, butyloctenal sounds the trumpet for the attack.

As scientists reveal the extraordinary complexity of insect pheromones, it has emerged that weaver ants are not only using chemical 'words', but various combinations of these, to create different 'phrases' in a way that is practically a form of chemical syntax. It might seem surprising that these tiny, seemingly robotic creatures should have evolved such a sophisticated level of communication. But then weaver ants have been around for more than 30 million years and have spread across the Old World tropics from Africa to Australia, and the secret of their success is probably their remarkably efficient chemical communication.

5

Vibration, Electricity and Touch

Streaking through the clear blue waters of the Bahamas the pair of dolphins seemed to be dancing, gracefully paralleling each other's every move. The female was moving very fast but the male, with body arched in an S-shape and neck outstretched, kept perfect time with her, swimming belly to belly and occasionally caressing her with his pectoral fins. Abruptly the female changed momentum. She turned over and, swimming upside-down, started to rub her body against his and head-butt him, while he hung upright in the water. To me, a human outsider, her movements still appeared to be part of a courtship dance, but in dolphin terms the meaning was very different. By rubbing against him and head-butting him, she was rejecting his advances, perhaps telling him that she wasn't yet sexually receptive. And in a final gesture, which speaks for itself, she turned from her suitor, slapping his face with her tail as she swam away.

OPPOSITE | A spider's web is like a giant sensory organ. At the centre a female awaits the tell-tale vibrations of prey struggling to escape or a male coming to court her.

Electricity is far more than a weapon for electric eels.

WE DON'T JUST use our eyes, ears and noses to gather information – our whole bodies can act as receivers. Physical contact is a very potent form of communication. Licking and grooming keep offspring clean, but have also evolved into a powerful way of expressing affection. Even among adults of many social species, nuzzling, rubbing, grooming and stroking are ways of greeting or reassuring others and of appeasing aggressive individuals. Biting, hitting or slapping, which primarily serve to inflict damage, can also be used to send a message. Many animals nip their offspring to chastise them and a slap or bite can reprimand a suitor, but used in jest a nip or a pounce can also be an invitation to play. Tactile signals are very familiar to us, yet we still know surprisingly little about them.

There are other channels of communication that are so different from ours that for a long time we didn't even know they existed. Now technology is taking us far beyond our own sensory realm and revealing a world of strange sensations. Reports of people being stunned by electric eels have long intrigued us, but now we are discovering that electricity is far more than a weapon. It is both a versatile and a rather private channel of communication used by just a few groups of fish. It is also a very short-range system so that even members of the exclusive electric club can only confer when in close contact – a distance of about half the fish's body-length. Just imagine having a perceptual world which extends no further than your outstretched arm!

Even more hidden from us were vibrations. This isn't a channel which humans sense very easily and so we have been largely unaware of seismic signalling between animals until now. Yet vibration may be one of the oldest forms of animal communication. Scientists who have studied fossils of primitive ear and jaw structures believe that the earliest land mammals 'heard' only through vibrations. Now we are discovering that animals, ranging from tiny insects to enormous elephants, may still be talking in this ancient tongue.

A mother uses her trunk to reassure her calf, scold it or just chivvy it along.

TOUCH

In the dense forests of the northern Congo, the Odzala National Park stretches for hundreds of miles. It is criss-crossed by ancient paths worn smooth by the passage of elephants over countless generations. The paths get bigger and turn into open boulevards as they approach Maya Nord, a huge marshy clearing in the forest called a 'bai', where elephants come to bathe and drink. But they remain wary: these bais are windows in the forest where ivory poachers may lurk. Experienced members of the herd repeatedly lift their trunks high to catch the tell-tale scent of humans. I was with conservationist Jean-Marc Froment and a film crew, and we had been watching a group of eight elephants led by an impressive matriarch. Nestled between them was a tiny calf, probably only a few months old. After drinking their fill, the

OVER PAGE | Elephants in Maya Nord in northern Congo. Elephants are vulnerable to poachers in these clearings and head for the safety of the trees if they catch the scent of humans.

elephants started to head back into the forest when suddenly the matriarch upped the pace. The wind had changed direction and they had probably caught our scent from the hide on the edge of the clearing. The older elephants hurried away but, left in the rear, the little one stopped, seemingly unsure of what to do. One female, probably his mother, turned back, reached out her trunk and gave him a gentle but firm push. It appeared to be both a sign of reassurance and a clear message that he should keep up with the rest of the herd. He responded immediately, though his mother continued to chivvy him along, holding his tail and steering him with her trunk until they reached the safety of the trees.

Touch requires that the sender of the message be in physical contact with the receiver, which means that most tactile signals are friendly as we reach out to greet or reassure each other.

Elephants use a wide range of smells and sounds (Chap 1, p.15, Chap 2, p.32) to communicate but they are also very much contact animals; family members often stand touching while resting or drinking, leaning and rubbing their bodies together or reaching out to touch one another with their trunks. The elephant's trunk is marvellously sensitive and expressive: mothers often touch and embrace their calves with their trunks or give them a quick slap to discipline them; youngsters playfully wrestle with their trunks and courting elephants may caress their partners or intertwine trunks. When two elephants approach each other they frequently hold their trunks out in greeting. Elephants may touch trunks, or a lower-ranking individual may reach and insert its trunk into the mouth of its superior in a behaviour reminiscent of a calf's habit of putting its trunk into its mother's mouth to taste foods or when seeking reassurance.

Touch is a very direct, immediate and persuasive way of communicating. A wildebeest mother noses her new-born calf, encouraging it to stand up; a lioness gives her cub a gentle nip to reprimand it when it becomes too boisterous; a pair of zebras stand in friendly contact resting their heads on each other's backs. Many forms of tactile communication are second nature to us, too, and yet there is a great paucity of knowledge about its role. Although there have been some studies of touch in humans in the hope of finding new communication tools for people afflicted with deaf-blindness, research still concentrates overwhelmingly on

In greeting, a low-ranking elephant often puts its trunk into the mouth of a higher-ranking individual. This behaviour is reminiscent of a calf's habit of putting its trunk into its mother's mouth to taste food or ask for reassurance.

the visual and acoustic channels, and our knowledge of the use of touch among animals is often just anecdotal.

There are many advantages to tactile communication. Other forms of communication require specialised organs, but we sense touch with our entire bodies. The skin covers an area over a thousand times that of the retina of the eye and is plentifully supplied with nerve-endings. It provides a nearly continuous sensitive surface which registers temperature changes, pain and pressure. Using the sensation of pressure to communicate may seem rather limited but in fact it is both rich and versatile. Just think how much we can tell if someone puts their hand on our arm. With our eyes closed we could say if the touch was affectionate, seductive, protective, a caution, or a reprimand.

When we have a conversation on the street, we must filter out the noise of passers-by, of traffic, wind or rain, perhaps even of a pneumatic drill. If we look across a room to smile at someone, we must catch their eye even if there are people milling in between or bright lights which dazzle us. But with touch, there are no such impediments to communicating and it is highly directional – if I touch you on the arm, there can be no mistaking who my message is intended for. Touch requires that the sender of the message be in physical contact with the receiver, which means that most tactile signals are friendly. They often indicate a special relationship between two individuals, like birds who preen their mates or those all-important contacts between a mother and her offspring from the moment of birth.

Physical contact is important among animals that raise their young and plays an important role in developing a close bond between a ewe and her lamb.

What brings a ewe and a newly born lamb into a position where the lamb can suckle? Experiments have shown that although sound, vision and smell all play a role, mother and baby achieve this through a step-by-step process of mutual touch. As soon as the lamb is born, the ewe will rise and turn to lick it, first on the head and forequarters. The lamb bleats and tries to stand while its mother gives a low rumbling sound to quieten it. The licking reduces its initial attempts to stand up. The ewe circles the lamb, keeping it in front of her as she cleans it, and when the lamb begins to rise to its feet its muzzle tends to make contact with its mother's front legs, neck or face. The lamb then tries to push its muzzle under the dam and as it feels its face and eyes covered and pressed against her underbelly it automatically tilts up its muzzle, extends its neck and begins to make sucking movements and search for the teat. Experiments show that this response is more vigorous if the lambs are not able to see. When the ewe feels the lamb's head pushing against her belly, she arches her back, lowers her tail and moves her hind leg outwards in order to expose the teat.

The use of physical contact to communicate is widespread among animals which raise their young. Licking and grooming keep offspring clean, healthy and free of parasites but have evolved into a way of expressing affection, even among adults of many social species; nuzzling, nibbling, rubbing, grooming and stroking are a way of bonding with, or appeasing, other individuals. For most primates, who spend a lot of time in close proximity to other members of their group, it is important that individuals try to stay on good terms. On average, primates spend about 20 per cent of their waking time grooming each other. It not only keeps them clean but also cements relationships and may be an equivalent of human gossip. When chimpanzees rest, they clump together in small groups and groom their friends and if they meet up after any period of separation the first thing they do is settle down for a good grooming session.

Grooming is especially important between male chimpanzees. All the males in a group are closely related and have to work together to defend their community's range. Grooming is vital for developing a strong sense of solidarity, but internal politics are also revealed by grooming preferences. Males form special alliances in an attempt to work their way up the hierarchy and individuals take to grooming each other as if sealing a secret agreement. None the less, if the dominant male suddenly appears on the scene it can be prudent for them to turn their attention to grooming him instead! If a dominant male feels his authority is in question he will usually perform a dramatic display to remind everyone who is boss, charging around tearing at undergrowth and sometimes slapping others as he goes by. Afterwards other members of the group will often gather round like adoring fans to groom him.

Common marmosets (*Callithrix jacchus*) live in extended family groups of between four and fifteen individuals, in which only one female breeds. All the other members of the group help to rear the two sets of twins born each year. Older members often lick the young to keep them clean, but licking is also used as a form of greeting between adults. Relationships between group members are very important and young marmosets enjoy an extended childhood during which they spend much of their time playing, wrestling and chasing through the branches. Play sessions may be initiated by a youngster stretching out a hand and touching or pushing one of its chums, or by one clapping both hands on another. They may give their playmate a quick playful bite before running away in the hope of being pursued. Sometimes, if

things start to get too boisterous and there is a chance that one of the youngest could get hurt, an adult may chastise the juveniles with a cuff – a quick, superficial blow – and if that is not enough to calm things down, a sharp bite to the neck may follow.

Like primates, most members of the horse family, Equidae, are highly social and once again tactile signals are essential for bonding between members of a group. Plains zebra (*Equus burchelli*) live in permanent groups of a male and his harem of females. Unusually for social animals, members of the group are not related and offspring of both sexes leave their natal group when they reach maturity. Despite the lack of blood ties between adults, life is generally harmonious. A characteristically amicable pose is standing in pairs, whereby two individuals stand alongside each other head to tail, or looking over each other's shoulder and resting their heads on each other's back. In this position they obligingly swish their tails and keep the flies away while simultaneously co-operating to survey 360 degrees for any sign of danger. Grooming is also an important element of zebra social life. Standing in pairs, and using their incisor teeth and lips, the zebras simultaneously scrape and nibble each other's neck, shoulders and back. This intimate nuzzling is frequent between mothers and their foals and between young siblings, but it also occurs between individuals of unequal rank. The initiative is usually taken by the low-ranking individual in an attempt to curry favour and he approaches cautiously, head outstretched and ears cocked. The dominant animal may respond in a similar fashion and the two will then start mutual grooming but he may scorn the approach by turning away or baring his teeth, a threat which says he wants to be left alone.

It is not just mammals which use touch to communicate – a surprising number of insects, arachnids, and crustaceans are also very touchy-feely. It seems that male fiddler crabs use touch to get their potential mates in the mood. Once the male has attracted the female by waving, he climbs on top of her carapace from the rear, then edges forward until he is almost completely covering her. When he has her in his embrace he will tap and stroke her carapace with his huge claw, and in species with pile in this region, he

OPPOSITE ABOVE | The equivalent of gossiping? Grooming among chimpanzees is a way of making friends.

BELOW | The young black tufted ear marmosets are raised in the bosom of an extended family. Licking keeps them clean and is also a form of greeting among adults.

'Standing in pairs' – this is one way zebras show friendship.

will pluck at it. While his claw is plucking away, his walking legs are continuously stroking the female's carapace, the combined effect of which seems to render her completely motionless. After a few minutes of this sensual 'massage', she is so still that he can flip her upside down and hold her at an angle to the ground with his walking legs, before engaging his reproductive appendages in her genital opening. Mating can last up to an hour or more, and some species of fiddler crab are so wrapped up in each other that they can be carefully approached and picked up while joined together.

Scorpions handle their courtship very differently. This time the male leads the female in a sinister mating waltz. The only species of scorpion to live in Britain is *Euscorpius flavicaudis*. A large, well-established colony lives in cracks in the walls of the Dockyard at Sheerness in Kent. The male of this species, and others belonging to the *Euscorpius* genus, grasps the female's pincers firmly in his and steps back and forth with jerky, trembling movements, while tapping the female's genital area with his foreleg. Then he stings her, several times in succession. The first strike can be anywhere on the female's body, but subsequent stings are invariably to a joint of one of the female's pincers. This lasts on average 13 minutes while the female remains still, though at first she may try to retreat. Occasionally the male may twist his sting in the wound but it is not known whether venom is injected or if it is purely a mechanical injury. Finally he deposits a package of sperm and pulls the female over it. The mating of scorpions can last several hours and it seems that elements of the male's bizarre ritual may be crucial in stimulating the female to accept the spermatophore.

Tactile signals are equally important for tail-less whip scorpions (order Amblypygi) who resolve disputes with a form of fencing which is highly ritualised. Males, and sometimes females, are often aggressive towards others of their sex and species. The sparring starts with individuals tapping each other irregularly with their legs in a provocative fashion. Then, a duel having been declared they move apart, stepping back a pace so that each animal can only just reach its opponent with one leg. The opponents now tap and stroke each other but this time each one precisely matches the other's moves. This goes on for a while and then abruptly stops as, with their sharp pedipalps (small forelimbs primarily used to handle food) flung wide, they lunge forward to engage in serious battle. An intense struggle ensues, with both animals grabbing at each other and pushing and pulling until finally one admits defeat. After that, if the two cross paths again all it takes is a characteristic wave of his leg by the winner and the subordinate animal beats a hasty retreat.

INSECT ENCOUNTERS

Insects often live in close proximity to each other and in addition to pheromones may use tactile signals to communicate at first hand. Among ants, simple messages are conveyed by tapping and stroking one another. By reaching out a foreleg to touch a nest-mate on a particular segment of its head, called the labium, which is roughly equivalent to the human tongue, a worker can induce another to regurgitate food. However, there is one insect for which the power of touch is so great that it not only influences an individual's behaviour but can literally transform it into a different creature: the desert locust.

Locusts have split personalities. The two types are so totally different in both appearance and behaviour that it was once thought that the two belonged to different species. One is a shy, retiring green creature which leads a solitary life, actively avoiding others of its kind. The other is black and yellow and so sociable that it forms some of the biggest gatherings on earth. A locust swarm can cover an area of 200 sq. km and contain over a billion locusts which collectively weigh over 10,000 tonnes. So how does the retiring Dr Jeykll turn into a rampant Mr Hyde?

Some detective work was required to find out what triggered the dramatic change. A series of experiments carried out at Oxford University by Steve Simpson and David Raubenheimer was designed to identify whether it is the sight, smell or contact with others – or a combination of these – that causes the phase change. The results show that, while the stimulation of the first two senses has some effect in combination, touch alone is the major stimulus. It does not even have to be the touch of another locust. Buffeting solitary locusts with small balls of papier-mâché is sufficient to trigger gregarious behaviour. So responsive are they to touch that, in the wild, even raindrops can cause them to gather together. When times are hard and food is patchy, the solitary locusts are forced to feed together. In the scramble for food, they bump and jostle one another and with every jolt their behaviour changes as they are 'brainwashed'. In order to find out which parts of their body responded to touch, the researchers at Oxford stroked solitary locusts for five seconds each minute for four hours on one of eleven body regions. They found that only stroking of the hind leg, which has sensitive hairs, caused significant 'gregarisation' and they called this area the G-spot.

OPPOSITE TOP AND MIDDLE | Touch is responsible for a Jekyll and Hyde transformation in locusts – a solitary green locust turns into a highly social and destructive black and yellow locust.

BELOW | A swarm of locusts can develop suddenly and devour 1,000 tonnes of crops a day.

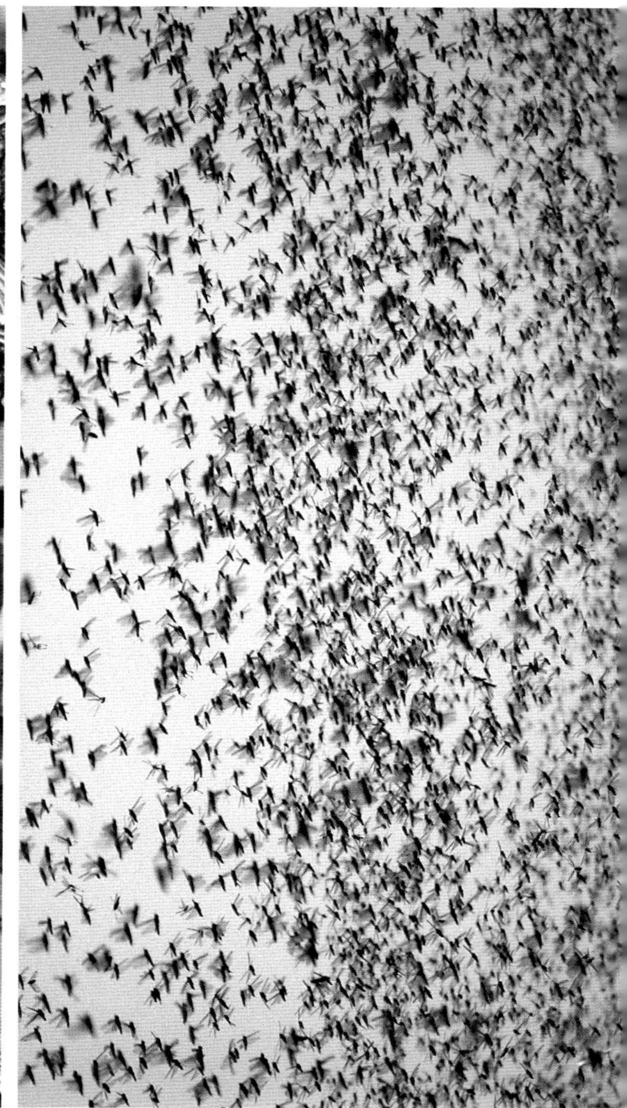

Within hours of jostling G-spots, the locusts have changed from being quiet loners to extreme extroverts, actively seeking each other out to form swarms of millions. The growing army now begins to change the way it looks, too, moulting out of its green to take on the black and yellow of a swarming locust. In their new guise the locusts wreak havoc, leaving devastation of biblical proportions in their wake. Each locust is capable of eating its own body-weight in 24 hours and a single swarm can devour over a thousand tonnes of crops in a day. A cohesion pheromone helps to keep swarming locusts together but eventually, despite their best efforts to aggregate, they find themselves losing contact with each other – dispersed by the environment (wind, weather or entering a densely vegetated habitat) or diminished by starvation, predation or disease.

Phase change from solitary to gregarious behaviour can even be transferred across generations. In effect, the mother uses her own experience of crowding to predict the likelihood that her offspring will find themselves in a crowd and predisposes their behaviour accordingly, so giving her young a head-start. Simpson and his colleagues found that after mating, female locusts dig a hole in the ground and lay their eggs (typically between 30 and 100) in a cylindrical pod. They surround the eggs with a frothy substance, secreted by their accessory glands, which helps to protect them by serving as a 'plug' and prevents them from drying out. While there is no evidence of a 'solitarising' agent in the eggs of solitary females, there is an agent in the foam produced by crowd-reared females that triggers eggs to hatch into gregarious individuals. While preventing locusts' tactile signals is well nigh impossible, analysis is under way to identify the active chemical agents in the foam which could be utilised in the battle against one of nature's most destructive creatures.

ELECTRIC SIGNALS

Along the coast of southern California, electric rays – otherwise known as torpedo rays – rise from the seabed at night, like Stealth bombers moving out on a mission. They can be up to two metres across and weigh some 90 kg and anything crossing their path had

An electric ray can be two metres across and deliver a shock of 600 volts in a fifth of a second.

better be wary. These are ruthless predators – they can strike like a lightning bolt, delivering as much as 600 volts in a fifth of a second, easily enough to stun a diver or immobilise and disorient their prey. It is said that the ancient Greeks used these rays for shock therapy.

Being able to zap another creature with electricity seems to belong to the realms of science fiction, but in fact all organisms generate electricity. Even humans have a faint electric aura created by the minute currents that carry signals through the body, keeping our hearts beating and our nerves firing. It is possible that the 'auras' some people claim to see are in fact due to this electrical energy. But the electric field around us and around most other living things is extremely weak – in plants it is no more than a billionth of a volt. As yet, only fish and a few amphibians are known to have harnessed electricity properly as a 'sixth sense'. They are all aquatic animals because water, unlike air, is a good conductor of electricity.

A knifefish lives in dark muddy waters of rivers and lakes in Central America and uses electricity to communicate.

Many fish, such as sharks, can detect electricity and use it to 'see', picking up the electric signal with special receptors along their lateral line. Only a few fish can generate their own external electricity with enough voltage to serve a useful purpose. Strongly electric species such as electric rays, stargazers, freshwater African electric catfish and the South American electric eels can all really pack a punch with outputs anywhere between 20 and 650 volts – that's nearly three times the force of British mains voltage. They use these powers with deadly effect, to defend themselves or to stun and kill prey.

Other fish are very low-powered by comparison. These weakly electric fishes belong to two principal groups: the gymnotiforms including knifefish, found in the rivers and lakes of South America, and the mormyrid fish of Africa such as the elephant-nose fish (*Gnathonemus peterseii*). These fishes produce electricity of only 0.1 to 0.75 volts – generally far too feeble to stun even the smallest prey. But they use their powers in more subtle ways and are the ones that really intrigued the biologists.

Hiding beneath the undercut banks of muddy rivers and lakes in Central and South America electric knifefish can grow up to about 90 cm, but most are about half this length, with flattened, elongated bodies like a blade. Pointing downwards in the water, they sway back and forth in gentle eddies and currents, feeding on aquatic insect larvae and small crustaceans. This may not appear to be a very lively existence but appearances can be deceptive. The pintail knifefish (*Brachyhypopomus pinnicaudatus*), the species we filmed with the assistance of Philip Stoddard's lab at Florida International University, begins its breeding season with sparks flying. When the mood is right, at the onset of the rainy season in May, the males start to display, courting the females with a spectacular electrical dance. These nocturnal fish cannot see each other in the dark and often murky waters but, as the male rests, floating in vegetation near the surface, he electrifies the water around him with a steady charge of about 70 short pulses a second, enticing the female towards him. As she approaches, he darts out of the plants and chases her. She circles behind him and he swiftly follows until the two elongate figures are gyrating in a three-dimensional dance. The male periodically cuts across the circle and runs his nose down the female's side. During the 'nose run' he turns on the charm in the form of intense bursts of electricity, about 200 rapid but long pulses a second, which appears to be a very potent stimulus to the female. After this frenetic foreplay, the male now slows the rate of his pulses, giving little chirps, and the pair back into the vegetation to spawn. The whole process only takes between two and ten minutes, but it may be repeated again and again, sometimes going on for more than two hours.

The fish feel the three-dimensional electric field around them, using thousands of tiny receptors. These receptors are scattered all over their bodies but are most densely concentrated around their heads where there can be as many as 80 per square millimetre. Portions of their brain are enlarged to process electrosensory information, so that the fish 'see' their surroundings through their skin by sensing any distortion in the electric field as they swim

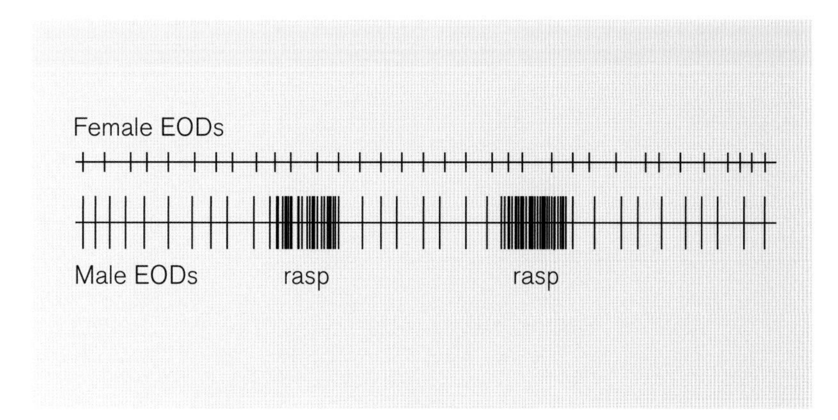

'Conversation' between male and female electric fish, shown by their different Electric Organ Discharges.

OPPOSITE | This graphic representation shows how electric fish 'see' their environment by sensing distortions in the electric field around them.

along. A rocky outcrop warps the field in one way; a fish swimming past warps it in another. To most of us, electricity is a very alien sense, but with the help of sensitive electrodes we are discovering not only how fish get a moving picture of their environment, allowing them to navigate, but we are also starting to piece together a whole new electric vocabulary.

The electric field of an electric fish is produced by a specialised structure called an 'electric organ' which, in most species, is located in the tail. It is made up of hundreds of muscle or nerve cells arranged in series like the batteries of a torch. The output of this organ is called the electric organ discharge, or EOD. The particular pattern of energy emitted by a fish, its waveform and rate of discharge, conveys precise information about species or sex. Researchers studying a mormyrid curiously called the whale-faced marcusenius (*Brienomyrus brachyistius*), from Gabon in West Africa, found that the waveform of the EOD is all-important for recognising both species and sex. The electrical discharge of the species has a characteristic configuration but females produce a much shorter, higher-frequency burst of energy than males. During the breeding season a male will defend his nest site, letting everyone know he is there with a slow, steady stream of about ten EODs per second. Carl Hopkins from Cornell University tested males' responses to computer-generated playbacks of EODs given at random intervals and to normal EOD sequences of males and of females. Hopkins found that males responded to any playback, irrespective of time intervals, so long as the waveform was female

It's easy to understand how this elephant-nose fish got its name.

and of the right species. Apparently, for these fish, time intervals between EODs say something else. If a fish swims past a male's nest site and its waveform indicates that it is a female, the male will up his rate tenfold, 'calling' to her with a rapid burst of EODs, called 'rasps', in the hope of getting her attention. Thus the overall pattern of electricity produced by electric fish not only informs others of their species and sex; it also conveys information about their mood, in this case the male's eagerness to mate.

Electricity travels fast and the fact that signals can be switched on and off in an instant means that it is ideally suited for sending rapidly-changing messages in unpredictable situations. Sometimes an electrical signal can be a warning to others of the same species. In several species, a sharp burst of pulses indicates that an animal is liable to attack. The elephant-nose fish has a short fuse and its high-frequency burst of pulses is a challenge to be taken seriously. A subordinate fish must respond with a very slow pulse rate or even stop its discharge altogether if it wants to avoid trouble. If the challenge is given to an equal, it will often spark a similar response. The rivals quickly take up a vigorous fighting posture and move into attack mode, head-butting each other until one of them backs down. They also deliver lateral blows to each other's bodies, often involving biting, as evidenced by wounds and dislodged scales.

Some animals can do little to change their social position, but ghost knifefish (*Apteronotus* spp.) have electrical arguments to decide who is boss. Ghost knifefish live together in loosely associated groups at the bottom of rivers, where they hunt at night in rocky clefts for insect larvae and small crustaceans. In each group one male is dominant and advertises the fact by giving out the highest rate of electrical discharge – 900 pulses per second as opposed to the norm of around 800. The most sexually mature female will settle on the opposite extreme, dropping below 700, which is the average for females of the species. All the others in the group have intermediate frequencies, to avoid jamming. If one fish decides to challenge the dominant male he will begin to match its frequency. Responding to this insult, the dominant male zaps the fish with a sudden short burst of very high-frequency charge, up to 1,000 Hz (pulses per second). If the aggressor disregards this warning and continues to imitate the dominant male's elevated frequency, then a battle must be fought. Once engaged in fighting, the two males may spend an entire night literally locked jaw to jaw. If the challenger is successful he will earn the exclusive right to spawn.

Electricity is ideally suited for sending rapidly-changing messages in unpredictable situations.

The ability to produce and receive electricity has evolved independently in several groups of fish – for a variety of reasons such as hunting, defence and navigation – into a versatile and sophisticated channel of communication. Even so, it can expose an individual to danger and it's useful to be able to fall silent quickly if you think the wrong fish is listening. Max Westby from the University of Sheffield recounts how he was using electrodes to record the pulses of a knifefish, when he suddenly picked up the emission of an approaching electric eel. The knifefish, a close relative of the electric eel, detected it too and immediately shut off its electric discharge. Unfortunately for the knifefish, on this occasion it didn't stay quiet for long enough – perhaps it thought the danger had passed, and it resumed its electrical discharge. With his electrodes in the water the researcher witnessed what happened next: he recorded a series of high-voltage discharges, saw a great splashing and turbulence and then heard a continuous low-frequency buzz as the eel swam away. The knifefish's signal was heard no more.

ABOVE | A female stink bug calls to the male by tapping out a pattern of vibrations on a leaf with her abdomen. These graphic representations show how the vibrations travel along branches and stems to the male who then follows the signal to find her. Using special equipment we can pick-up these vibrations, so I found myself eavesdropping on a remarkable conversation between stink bugs.

BELOW | The stink bug is one of the most destructive pests in the world.

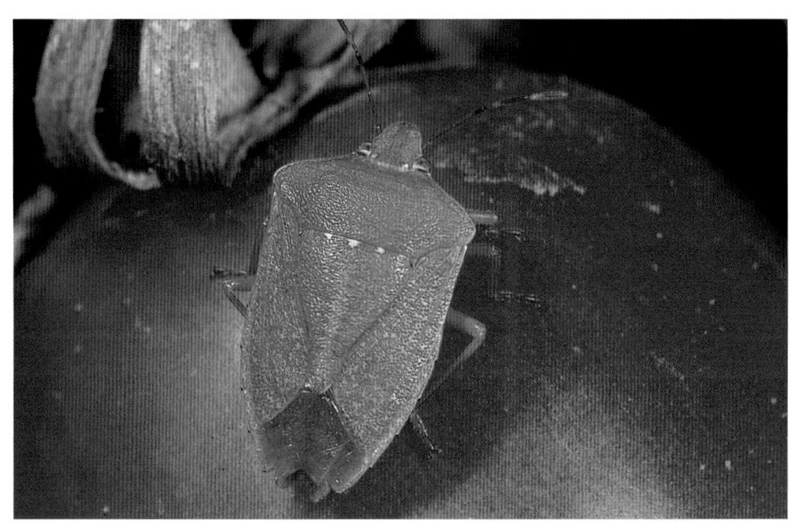

VIBRATION

We might not be aware of it but all around us, in our gardens, fields and hedgerows, there is a parallel universe which is trembling with a multitude of minute conversations. We tend to think of wildlife as the large, obvious animals but the majority of animals on our planet are insects, maybe some 10 million different species. It is estimated that there are as many as 10 quintillion – 10,000,000,000,000,000,000 – insects alive at any given time and all of them are busily sending messages.

In May the romantic vineyards and fields along the Mediterranean coast of Slovenia are alive with small bright green bugs. The southern green stink bug (*Nezara viridula*) is originally from Ethiopia, but now it is found right across tropical and subtropical regions of the world. Despite their name, stink bugs give off only a mild, inoffensive smell if disturbed and it's by no means the main reason for their dubious reputation. Stink bugs are guilty of something far worse: they belong to the family Pentatomidae, whose members are notorious for being some of the most widespread and destructive crop pests in the world. In late spring in Slovenia stink bugs have especially hearty appetites, munching their way through the grapevines, beans and tomatoes that cover the fertile hillsides. But food isn't the only thing on their agenda at this time of the year. Quite literally, love is in the air.

Wafts of inviting pheromones are released by males while out dining, in a bid to attract passing females. Females respond eagerly to the scented trails that swirl on the gentle Mediterranean breeze. There is a sense of urgency – stink bugs must mate and produce offspring in a matter of weeks, but how do they find the source of the beguiling invitation? Standing in a vineyard imagining the world from a stink bug's perspective, it suddenly becomes apparent that for a very small bug of less than a centimetre it's a very, very big world. Pinpointing the precise location of a male sitting on a single leaf among acres of foliage must be like trying to meet up with a friend under a tree in the Amazon. When she senses the male's pheromone, the female flies towards its source, lands on a leaf and starts to 'sing'. This isn't singing in any ordinary sense

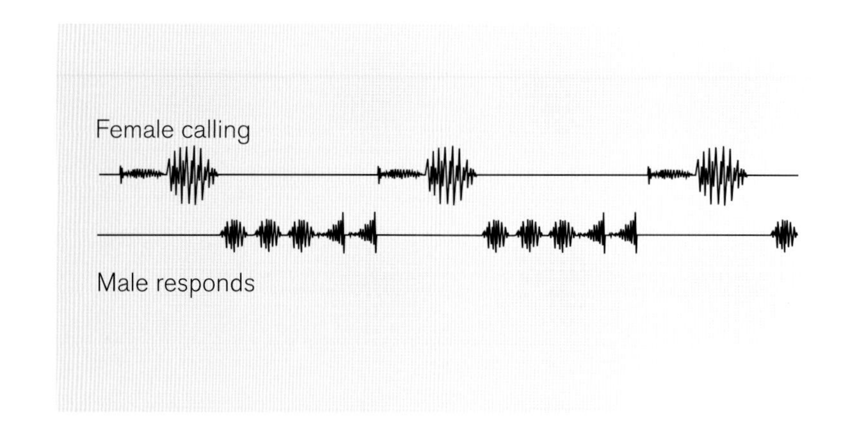

A sonagram of a stinkbug 'conversation'.

– she is vibrating not her vocal cords but the leaf she sits on, her abdomen trembling as it presses against the surface. She calls to the male using different kinds of vibration – a short introductory pulse precedes an intense narrow-band burst, then a series of separate broad-band pulses is followed by a five-second pause. And she repeats her song over and over again.

The vibrations are of very low frequency (about 100 Hz). Such small creatures can only produce vibrations which would be effectively transmitted through the air as sound if they are of high frequency. For example, a bug that is only a centimetre long can produce sounds of relative intensity only above 10,000 Hz. This phenomenon is obvious in our everyday life: bass notes can be reproduced by large loudspeakers and high-frequency tones by smaller ones. But the high-frequency sounds produced by small insects are strongly attenuated as they travel through vegetation, and singers are easily overheard by their predators, so instead many small insects use the plants they dwell on to carry messages in the form of vibrations. At speeds of 30–100 metres per second the vibrations travel rapidly through the leaf and into the side stem, then carry along the main stem and radiate out along branches and down into the roots. Here they connect with the root systems of other plants, passing on the same rhythm of pulses into stems and leaves until gradually the signal gets weaker and finally fades out altogether.

The male sits on his leaf, listening carefully with his feet. If the pattern of the vibrations tells him that the sender is a female of the right species, he will send his own vibrations back and start to move towards her. But the vibrations also give him clues as to her whereabouts. Like 'getting warmer, getting colder' in a game of hide and seek, he stops at each junction and straddles two stems to listen. There, he waits for the female's calls, and moves in the direction of the vibrations. The female's low humming is punctuated by perfect pauses in which the male responds with a song of his own in order to keep the female singing. He repeats a very regular rhythm of narrow-band pulses and then switches to broad-band pulses, each starting deep and getting higher. Broad-band elements comprise several different frequencies and are quite 'noisy', whereas narrow-band elements are purer tones.

The team of researchers at the National Institute of Biology of Ljubljana in Slovenia, led by Andrej Cokl and Meta Virant-Doberlet, has been investigating how such small insects talk to each other. Their highly sensitive equipment allowed us to eavesdrop on the stink bugs' conversations – which can only be detected by vibrometers using reflected laser beams to record the minute vibrations. These are then stored on a computer and can be converted to sounds detectable to the human ear. Suddenly we enter the stink bug's world and the tiny vibrations become a real conversation: distinctive humming sounds exchanged in a regular, meaningful pattern.

The female stink bug's low humming is punctuated by perfect pauses in which the male responds with a song of his own.

Different songs are used by males and females – males respond to a female's calling with a courtship song, and females will change their tune to a courtship song as a male approaches. Females which are not receptive to a male's advances will give a 'noisy' low burst of vibration which is especially effective at close range and stops male courting. If a singing male hears another male calling to the same female, he will switch his song to the rival song, and both males will alternate with rival song pulses until one of them moves away.

The new technology which has enabled us to listen in on these previously inaudible conversations is revealing just how widely used vibrations are in the animal kingdom. Many insects, spiders, frogs, crabs and some mammals are now known to employ seismic signals and almost any substrate or medium can act as an

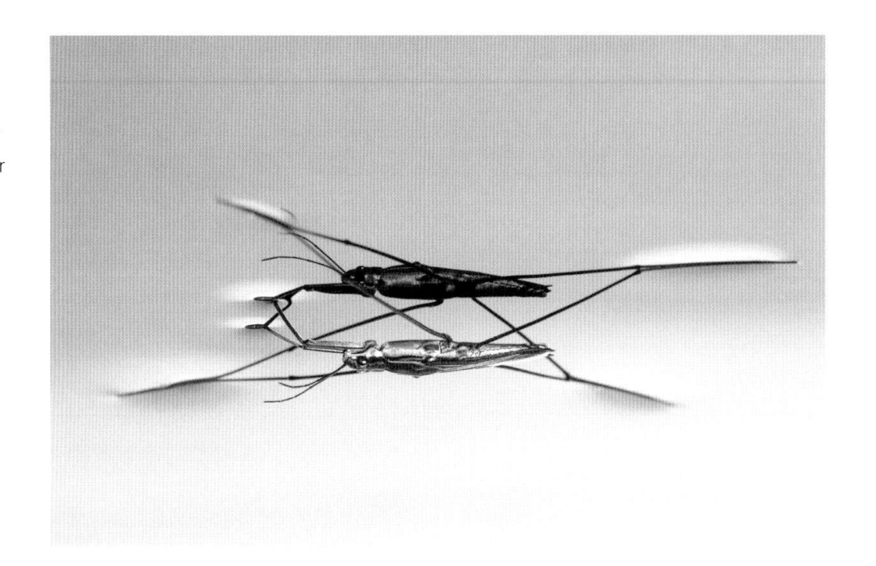

Water striders talk in ripples. By tapping the surface of the water and producing a particular pattern of ripples they identify themselves as male or female.

instrument. Water striders (family Gerridae), for instance, talk in ripples. The oily pads on their feet allow them to skate across the surface of ponds and lakes, using vibration receptors in the joints of their six legs to detect small insect prey struggling with the surface tension. But they also send messages to each other by tapping the water surface with their legs and producing ripples. Males proclaim their sex with a barrage of 90 ripples a minute while females respond with a slow succession of only ten.

Lying just below the surface of the water a crocodile flutters its flanks, its twitching body sending reverberations out across a pool. They may seem like the silent type but crocodiles are great communicators, combining infrasound and vibrations to send messages through their watery surroundings. One of the most widely used signals is 'head-slapping'. The crocodile rests with its lower jaw on the surface of the water and slaps its upper jaw down, causing a loud pop and splash as the jaws meet. It is thought to be given by the top-ranking crocodile in an area and certainly commands attention. 'Head-slapping' is sometimes followed by exhaling bubbles from their nostrils which may also be a form of communication. We have a long way to go in deciphering such signals but what we do know is that crocodiles have pressure receptors all over their bodies capable of sensing very low-frequency sounds and vibrations through the water.

Alligators also produce an infrasonic vibrational signal, just prior to bellowing, which is thought to serve to attract alligators of the opposite sex and possibly to disperse animals of the same sex. The signal is so powerful that water 'dances' up around the alligator's torso as much as 25 cm above the surface. It has a frequency of about 10 Hz, which should theoretically travel long distances underwater. It is possible that the vibrational signal in association with the bellowing display allows females to locate males during the courting season.

Previously, only insects were known to use plant-borne vibrations, but Kenneth Barnett, a reptile enthusiast, observed that when he was handling his pet veiled chameleon (*Chameleo calyptratus*) one day it shivered in response, producing a distinct vibration which emanated from its body just in front of its front legs. It wasn't shaking in fear but rather sending a signal of distress. With the male alone and undisturbed on a plant, no vibrations were detected. When a male was placed on a plant with a receptive female, it commenced a courtship display, changing its coloration, flattening its body, and also producing a series of vibrational signals. Signals were produced in groups of 1 to 14, each beginning with a series of high-pitched short ones typically above 105 Hz, followed by a longer one below 90 Hz, frequencies which would lie comfortably within the vocal range of a baritone singer. But none of these signals were audible to a person standing a metre from the lizard and as chameleons are less sensitive to airborne sounds than humans, the lizards in the study must have been sensing the vibrations through the branch.

Mud rather than water or vegetation is the preferred medium for white-lipped frogs (*Leptodactylus albilabris*) in Puerto Rico. A researcher attempting to capture some calling males found that every time he approached, however carefully, the frogs instantly fell silent even though he was still some distance away. It appears that the frogs could pick up the sensation of the ominous advancing footsteps through the ground. Now researchers have turned the tables on them: using ultra-sensitive geophones once employed by troops to listen for footfalls in the jungles of Vietnam, they can pick up the frogs' strange thumps. These thumps aren't made by clumsy frogs moving about, they are a deliberate and distinctive courtship call to the females. The mountain streams, marshes and ditches they live in are shared by many other species of frog who are noisy neighbours. At night there is such a racket of croaking going on around them that white-lipped frogs employ a different tactic to make themselves heard: after rain, they bury their rear in the mud and when they croak in this position their vocal pouch expands explosively, striking the ground and generating an impact that zooms through the earth at roughly 100 metres per second. It is guaranteed to get a female's attention, and also that of neighbouring males who respond in kind, producing a chorus of vibrations.

Elephants stand on their toes which rest on a big cushion of fatty tissue like a waterbed.

Vibrations can travel great distances, which could make them a useful source of information for animals that tend to be widely dispersed. Elephants often move in the same direction even when they are beyond hearing range, which suggests that they can in some way sense movements of distant herds. Researchers in the field have reported elephants behaving quite oddly at times when another herd is in the vicinity. They don't scan the horizon, raise their trunks or flap their ears. Instead, they tend to freeze and sometimes raise and lower a foot. Elephants actually stand on their toes which rest on a big cushion of fatty tissue like a waterbed. This is what allows them to walk so quietly but also perhaps to pick up vibrations travelling through the ground. Tiny movements could be picked up through their soles, causing their feet to quiver like jelly and stimulating specialised Pacinian cells. These cells are vibration-sensitive and have recently been found densely packed in the tips of elephant trunks (which, incidentally, may account for the reports of elephants resting their trunks on water pumps to gauge whether they are switched on). Now zoologists are trying to discover whether elephants have the same cells in their feet. Although it is still speculation, if they do sense vibrations with their feet, then elephants may be able to gather much useful information through the ground. They may be able to gauge the size of an approaching herd and the distance of another herd, or sense the trembling caused by a charge or a stampede away from danger.

The enormous feet of this kangaroo rat are used to drum out messages to other kangaroo rats.

But it is not only the vibrations caused by movement that elephants may be aware of. When an elephant produces a loud low-frequency contact rumble (Chap 1, p.15, Chap 2, p.32) a similar seismic wave is transmitted through the ground. This seismic wave travels more slowly than the accompanying sound wave but a lot further. It is perhaps detectable at distances of up to 16 km. Although elephants are unlikely to receive any detailed information in this way, one theory suggests they may be able to judge the distance of the caller by the time interval between hearing the rumble and feeling it through the ground, in rather the same way that we count the seconds between seeing a flash of lightning and hearing the thunder to determine how far away a storm is.

Study of seismic communication in elephants is in its infancy. Much more is known about the way in which banner-tailed kangaroo rats (*Dipodomys spectabilis*) use vibrations to keep in touch over distance. These small rodents are perfectly adapted to life in the more arid regions of western and south-western USA. They lead a solitary life, eating seeds which provide them with both nutrition and sufficient water to survive in their inhospitable habitat (their kidneys have four times the concentrating ability of human kidneys). Periodically, kangaroo rats will disappear into the large mounds which are their homes and stamp their enormous hind feet on the ground. In open deserts where there are few places to hide from the watchful eyes and ears of predators, ground-thumping is a subtle way of communicating with others of your species and this is the kangaroo rat's way of advertising its territory. Like any successful neighbourhood watch system, familiarity with neighbours – who are often extended family members – is vital if you are to distinguish them from strangers. In the case of kangaroo rats, that means the way you thump. The thumps of their feet are grouped into short bursts called foot-rolls and several foot-rolls are combined to make a sequence. Each individual has its own foot-drumming pattern, or signature, which is unique – both in the number of drums in the first foot-roll and the number of foot-rolls per sequence. On hearing the drumming of a neighbour, the rats tend to hurry into their mound and drum out a response, but will soon re-emerge and resume their normal activity. When a stranger is in the neighbourhood, the rats drum at much higher rates for prolonged periods. This is usually enough to see the intruder off and only as a last resort will they emerge, approach the challenger and engage in foot-drumming exchanges until one party backs down.

By drumming, kangaroo rats inadvertently advertise themselves as dinner.

Gopher snakes (*Pituophis melanoleucus*) share the kangaroo rats' environment and, like all snakes, they are acutely sensitive to vibrations in the ground, picking up the tiniest trembling with their lower jaw and skull in order to locate prey. By drumming, kangaroo rats inadvertently advertise themselves as dinner. Sometimes it's better to meet a problem head-on and, on encountering a snake, the rats drum furiously, adding extra foot-rolls to the end of the sequence. It was previously thought that they were sounding the alarm to warn neighbours, but as they also thump the ground when there are no neighbours around, researchers now believe that kangaroo rats are talking to the snake itself, using a language it can understand. A snake relies on stealth and surprise to catch its prey and the drumming tells the snake that its movements are being carefully monitored. When the snake knows it has been spotted, the game is over and it usually gives up the hunt.

Unwittingly we, too, alert animals to our presence with the vibrations we make when we move. Houses that have stood empty for long periods of time may harbour the pupae of cat fleas which can lie dormant for months, even years, listening for the right vibrations made by a cat or human walking past; they then emerge and leap on to their host. This might come as an unpleasant surprise when moving into a new home, but it's no more serious than that. Alerting others to your presence with your footsteps can have far more serious consequences – not just for prey but for predators too. The Ethiopian wolf (*Canis simensis*), for instance, tiptoes around the Afro-alpine grassland playing 'grandmother's footsteps' with prey species, such as the giant molerat (*Tacyoryctes macrocephalus*) because, living underground, these rodents must be especially sensitive to footfalls above ground.

THE SPIDER'S WEB

The web of an orb spider is like an extended sensory organ; it is also a fatal trap. Members of the families Areneidae and Tetragnathidae use different textures of silk, from three or four sets of special glands called spinnerets, to construct intricate orb-shaped webs. First they spin the non-sticky support and radial lines and then sticky strands spiralling outwards from the centre. Spider silk may look very delicate but it is amazingly strong – in fact, the relative tension required to break it is far greater than for steel. The web itself also acts as an extended sensory organ, picking up any movements like an enormous trampoline and conveying their messages to the spider waiting on the web. Any passing insect which becomes ensnared is unlikely to escape and its struggles serve only to seal its doom. Alerted by the movement in the web the spider rushes to secure its victim, binding and immobilising the hapless insect with silken threads.

Male spiders must shake and tap the web with a very particular rhythm if they are to approach the female without being mistaken for prey. In order to study the different patterns of vibrations, researchers use a laser system coupled to a computer, called 'laser vibrometry'. As the web vibrates, different light intensities are reflected on to a solar cell, producing a change in voltage; these

changes are then assembled by the computer, which converts them into a pattern of vibrations. Every species has its own rhythm. The female spider reads the rhythm produced by the male, sensing the vibrations with structures called slit sensilla located on her ankle and middle leg and with tiny hairs on the joint between the middle leg and foreleg. Although the pattern of vibrations caused by the male plucking on the threads is quite unlike the erratic struggles of a desperate prey, he must still get the right password to tell the female that he is a male of the same species or he is doomed.

Males of one species of spider are doomed whatever they do. The Australian redback spider (*Latrodectus hasselti*) has a distinctive red or orange stripe across its back. Its underside is decorated with a characteristic hourglass mark, the coat of arms of its hazardous family. As with its renowned cousin the black widow, the bite of a female redback can be deadly, although there have been very few deaths since the introduction of antivenom in 1956. When courting a female, a male must start with platitudes as soon as he reaches the female's web – there are no second chances here. Moreover, there is no time to waste, as he may find as many as six other suitors also trying to impress her. In order to persuade her to choose him he must perform a variety of movements, flexing and extending his legs while walking, drumming and plucking at the web and rivalling the best belly dancer with rapid gyrations of his abdomen. Still, it may take up to eight hours of this to persuade the female redback that he is the mate for her. It is likely that his movements carry information across the web which allows her to assess his qualities as a mate. If he is found lacking, she will reject him, tossing him out of the web with a flick of her foreleg – and as she is three times his size there is no point in arguing.

If he does manage to impress her, his fate will be far worse – he is likely to be eaten alive. The male redback's sex organs are at the front of his head, encased in structures called 'palps' that have been described as resembling a tiny pair of boxing gloves. Coiling out from each is a long tube, the embolus, which he inserts into the female just below her 'waist' where her abdomen connects to her

OPPOSITE ABOVE | An Australian redback spider delivers a deadly bite like its cousin the black widow.

BELOW | A characteristic hourglass marking is evident on the underside of the female black widow spider. It's a dangerous business for the male to court the female as she is three times his size and deadly.

Leaf-cutter ants enlist the help of small hitch-hikers which protect them from parasitic flies as they carry leaf fragments back to the nest.

thorax. Then suddenly, in a profoundly macabre act, he somersaults over the female and lands directly in front of her mouth, offering himself up for sacrifice. He continues to transfer his sperm as she gives him the kiss of death, slowly digesting him with enzymes secreted from her mouth.

Other female insects may try to eat their mates from time to time but males normally make a concerted effort to escape, so why do redback males readily present themselves in front of the female's jaws? The simple reason is that male redbacks have a hard life. Eighty per cent die while searching for a female and with a lifespan of only a few weeks it is very unlikely that a male who has been successful in wooing a female will ever get a second chance. So he gives all he's got in the one act of sex which will ensure the transfer of his genes. By offering himself up to be consumed by his mate, he can prolong the sex act by another fifteen minutes or so, making it twice as likely that he will father a new generation of spiderlings.

How do we as humans begin to decipher the mysteries of spider communication? Again, new technology can help us. The wandering spider, *Cupiennius salei*, is found in Central America and, like stink bugs, uses plants to channel messages. Their

favourite dwellings are banana plants, which also turn out to be excellent message boards on which to tap out signals. Wolfgang Schuech and Friedrich Barth electronically synthesised the vibrations of male spiders and tested the females' reaction to them. Placed on a vibrating platform, the females were played different versions of male courtship in which various parameters of the waveform were altered, using a computer to find out what aspects make them respond with their own vibration of acceptance. The results showed that only the syllables created by abdominal vibrations appear to be essential to courtship; it is thought that pedipalpal signals may be more involved in telling the female the whereabouts of the male. The most crucial aspects of the syllables created by abdominal vibrations are their frequency, duration, repetition rate and the length of the gaps between subsequent syllables. But no single parameter contains the magic word guaranteed to get a response from the female. Instead, many variables turn out to influence how attractive the male vibrations are.

ANT BROADCASTS

Vibrations spread out in all directions from the source, rippling through the substrate whether that is a plant, water, the earth, or the silken threads of a spider's web. They make a perfect public broadcast system and are used by some animals to co-ordinate the behaviour of many individuals – millions, in fact.

Leaf-cutter ants (*Atta* spp.) are found from northern Texas right down to Argentina and live in nests that can be six metres high and cover 200 square metres. As many as five to eight million ants may live together in one colony – a city of ants with a population larger than Bangkok. When watching leaf-cutter ants, like Gulliver in Lilliput one looks down on a world in miniature, as a constant procession of ants march in and out of their city armed with leaf fragments. Their main occupation is cultivating the fungus gardens which are their source of food. There is constant activity – aerial walkways and intersections buzz with passing traffic as a steady supply of leaf fragments are brought and made into a pulp with saliva, to be used as compost. The ants are so industrious that they can denude a whole tree in a single night, but watching them you can't help wondering how everyone knows what they are supposed to be doing. Ants speak several different 'languages', pheromones being the most important (Chap 4, p.153). They are also extremely sensitive to vibrations in the ground or other substrates and recently the role of vibrations in co-ordinating their activities has been investigated.

In leaf-cutter ants there are many different castes of workers – a single colony may comprise workers of which the largest are 200 times the size of the smallest. Not surprisingly, the big hefty workers are better suited to some tasks while the minims, the smallest, are better suited to others. When out foraging for leaf matter, some workers perform amazing feats – the human equivalent of carrying a 300-kg load over a distance of about 15 km at a speed of 24 km/hour – which outstrips any human world record. Not all ants are involved in cutting and carrying leaf fragments, however. Some are scouts who look for good new sources of leaf material, some have jobs clearing trails, others transport plant sap and others still may be involved in reinforcing the chemical trail.

When harvesting leaves, some workers use a specialised organ called a gaster to stridulate (Chap 2, p.38), which produces high-frequency vibrations. These vibrations are conducted into the leaf through the ant's mandibles and legs and have the effect of ripping through leaves like mini-chainsaws. However, while these make smoother cuts, it appears that they don't actually increase the speed or efficiency of cutting. In an experiment designed to determine the purpose of stridulation, researchers offered the ants different kinds of leaves. They found that the number of ants stridulating increases not according to the toughness of the leaf but according to its desirability. The stridulations produce vibrations that pass through the ants' mandibles, into the leaves and along the stems of the plants. On picking up these signals, nearby workers hasten to respond and move towards the source. If ants have been deprived of the opportunity to harvest leaves the proportion that stridulates will be very high for a while, after which it decreases dramatically. This suggests that the primary purpose of the stridulation is to recruit others to the cutting area.

Minim workers are too small to cut leaf fragments but they too have a job to do. At the cutting site and along the foraging trail they stop and check leaf-carriers, climbing on to their backs or the leaf fragments to hitch a ride back to the nest site. The minims aren't being lazy, though – they are protecting the carriers who are too heavily laden to defend themselves against attacks from the parasitic phorid flies which attempt to lay their eggs in the workers, causing disruption on the trails and slowing down the whole process. Even workers who don't stridulate while cutting start to do so as they manoeuvre the leaf fragment into the carrying position, in order to call the minims to hop on board and watch their backs.

Vibrations can also act as an alarm system so that, if disaster strikes, leaf-cutters can rush to each other's aid. A German zoologist, Hubert Markl, discovered that in times of crisis, such as a cave-in of the nest during heavy rainfall, the trapped ants tap out a call for help. Those above ground can pick up the SOS signals, using extremely sensitive detectors in their legs, through as much as five centimetres of earth (which is something like the equivalent of 150 metres to us) and mount an immediate rescue operation to excavate their friends below.

OVER PAGE | Honey bees home in on nectar.

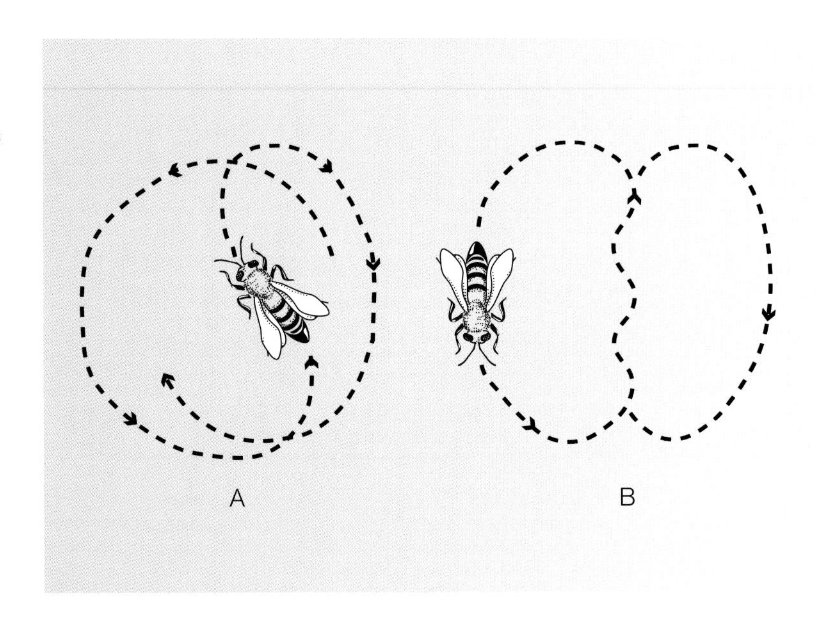

(A) The circle dance encourages others to go on reconnaissance missions in search of flowers. (B) The waggle dance tells others the exact location of flowers when they are found.

THE MYSTERY OF THE WAGGLE DANCE

Communication is the key to co-operation and enables some of the smallest animals to achieve extraordinary feats. Honeybees and their relatives the bumblebees fulfil the gargantuan task of pollinating most of the world's flowering plants. They live in colonies comprising a queen, up to two thousand males and thousands of female workers. The nectar and pollen they collect are stored away in the hexagonal cells of their waxy combs and made into honey. Millions of trips between flowers and the nest are required to make enough honey to fill a single jar.

The bees' efficiency in foraging depends on their ability to share information about the location of flowers. By dancing round in circles, scout bees encourage their sister bees to go on searching missions close to the hive but if a rich floral patch is found some distance away, the scouts perform a 'waggle dance'. The waggle dance is one of the most exceptional forms of communication in the animal kingdom – it appears to re-enact a bee's journey in miniature and, astonishingly, tells the others the direction, distance and quality of the nectar. It is a truly symbolic form of communication, a signal that provides information about something separated in both space and time.

Karl von Frisch won a Nobel Prize in 1965 for his pioneering work on the waggle dance and gained the honeybee a special place in the hearts and minds of biologists. The dancer dances up and down the wall of a vertical comb. She does a straight run, turns to the right and circles back to the starting point, then does another straight run, turns left at the top and circles back, repeating the pattern to create a figure of eight. During the straight run, the dancer waggles her body from side to side about fifteen times a second while vibrating her wings. As she dances, other bees gather behind her and follow her through the movements.

The critical part of the dance is the straight run. The direction and duration of the straight runs correlate closely with the direction and distance of the flower patch being advertised. Direction is given according to the position of the sun. Flowers located directly in line with the sun are represented by straight runs directly upwards, and any angle to the right or left of the sun's position is coded by a corresponding angle to the right or left of vertical. The distance of the food source is correlated with the duration of the run and the number of waggles – so that the further away the flowers, the longer the straight run and the slower the dance tempo. How follower bees detect these movements in the darkness of a hive remains a mystery. Von Frisch suggested two explanations: either the dancer generates vibrations that carry through the wax comb to the followers or the followers might touch the dancer. Measurements of the vibrations indicate that they are too weak to be a reliable source of information. Moreover, by using a robotic bee to perform the dance Axel Michelson from Odense University in Denmark found that it could still inform followers about the distance and location of flowers without making contact with the cone. From high-speed video it is possible to see that the followers touch the dancer with one or two antennae during the waggle run; this is likely to play a role but the waggling movements, which are quite violent, would make it difficult for followers to obtain precise information.

Recently Michelson and his colleagues started to investigate another possibility. During the straight run, the vibrations of the dancer's wings create a three-dimensional field of oscillating air-

Each bee has a brain about the size of a grass seed, so where does this collective wisdom come from?

flows. Could these be important in telling sister bees the direction of the food source? Measuring the air-flows is no easy task but Michelson and his team use a PIV system (Particle Image Velocimetry) whereby a laser beam is flattened into a thin sheet of light by passing it through a cylindrical lens. The sheet is then made visible by a special smoke machine so that air-flows in the same plane as the sheet can be detected according to the movements of the smoke particles. Photographs taken at very short intervals show the changing positions of the particles over time. The researchers discovered that there is a particularly strong air jet flowing directly out from behind the dancer. The way in which this jet hits the followers depends on their position relative to the axis of the straight run, leading to speculation that this may be how they pick up information on the direction and speed of the dancer. Michelson and his colleagues suggest that the waggling of the dancer's abdomen may serve to sweep the jet over the antennae of follower bees and that the jets of air may also carry odours from the flowers visited by the dancer, giving the others an indication of their quality.

The famous waggle dance is not only used to tell nest-mates about where to find food; it is also used to find a new home. In the late spring or early summer, when food is plentiful, a hive can quickly become overcrowded. Then the queen will upsticks, sending several hundred scout bees off in search of a new home. They are looking for a hollow in a tree, or a similar cavity, with a volume of at least 20 litres. It should have thick, strong walls and an opening no bigger than 30 sq. cm, be at least three metres above the ground and south facing. The scouts may find a dozen or more alternatives that more or less fit their requirements, but within a couple of days they are all agreed upon a single location.

Considering that each bee has a brain about the size of a grass seed, where does this collective wisdom come from? To find out, Tom Seeley from Cornell University and his student Susannah Buhrman tagged all 4,000 bees in a swarm with a number and a colour code. After around 66 hours of painstaking work, the researchers could simply sit back and watch the swarm. They found that the quality of the site influences the vigour of the dancing – the best sites producing a dance with the most waggle runs. But how do the bees compare alternative sites to reach a consensus about which is best? By tracking the behaviour of individual bees, the researchers made a crucial discovery. Scouts evaluate a site and dance accordingly but they do not switch allegiance between sites. If they fail to attract attention, they do not dance again and so the site rapidly loses all its support. This seemingly trivial observation means that the decision-making process doesn't become deadlocked and the best site is selected very quickly.

How bees evaluate a good home is still largely a mystery. However, using an ingenious set-up with treadmills, Seeley showed that bees take direct measurements to assess the volume of a potential home, based on the amount of walking they have to do to circumscribe the cavity.

From a human viewpoint, it seems amazing that more than a hundred individuals, especially ones with such tiny brains, can reach the right decision in a matter of hours. But by taking advantage of their large numbers, making a virtue of the fact that no one individual could possibly co-ordinate the proceedings and following a few simple rules, they combine to create a superorganism able to make sophisticated and accurate decisions.

6

Learning, Flexibility and Deception

Sunbathing in pools of early-morning light on the forest floor, ring-tailed lemurs sit upright with faces tilted to the sun, their arms resting casually on their knees. This tranquil attitude is deceptive – they are constantly on the lookout for harrier hawks or buzzards that may swoop from the skies at any moment. Anyone who spots an aerial predator immediately sounds the alarm to the others, uttering a piercing shriek. The alarm system works but it does depend on identifying the danger correctly. Youngsters are occasionally over-enthusiastic with their warnings, shrieking loudly when in fact it is only a harmless hook-billed vanga flying past or an innocent vasa parrot minding its own business.

OPPOSITE | The songs of birds can be very complex. Although born with the basics of their song, to develop it fully, songbirds (such as this reed warbler) must hear their parents sing.

PROPER COMMUNICATION SKILLS require an ability to produce the right signal; to produce it in the right context and to respond appropriately to the signals of others. How do animals learn to produce and respond to signals correctly? How much is nature, how much is nurture?

We know that many forms of both human and animal communication are fixed, instinctive, and directly linked to physiological state. A dog doesn't learn to growl or raise its hackles in order to send a message of aggression, any more than a baby has to learn how to cry in order to get its mother's attention. However, learning is involved in many forms of human communication, not least language. Not only do we learn our own language and perhaps foreign languages too, we develop new expressions and the meanings of words change over time. The ability to learn and to modify behaviour accordingly is generally regarded as a measure of intelligence.

A group of ring-tailed lemurs sunning themselves.

We now know that learning plays a crucial role in the development of some animals' signals, most notably the songs of birds and the calls of primates, and that their social environment is all-important. Moreover, animal signals are not necessarily fixed but can develop over time, and occasionally change radically over a very short time span, as we will see with the songs of humpback whales.

It takes ten years for long-tailed manakins to perfect their courtship dance. Males dance in pairs and jump up and down in a 'popcorn' display as part of their routine to impress the female.

LEARNING

As soon as their female spectator is settled, the male manakins begin their cartwheel display. Long-tailed manakins (*Chiroxiphia linearis*) are small Costa Rican birds who dance in duos to win the approval of their females. Richly attired with an iridescent red crown, deep black body and powder-blue back, and with two central tail feathers extended in a long, graceful arc, they leap into the air and spin backwards over each other in turn. This is just the warm-up. The show continues as the two males then take turns hopping up and down, side by side on a branch like a pair of jack-in-the-boxes, in what is called the 'popcorn' display. This is interspersed with interludes of floating, butterfly-like flight that flashes the electric-blue feathers atop their jet-black wings.

The performance is so complicated, and getting it absolutely right is so important, that it can take males ten years to perfect their dance! As fruit eaters, female manakins don't need the help of the males to raise the chicks, so the males have to work extra-hard to convince them of their worth. And they don't try to do it solo. Long-tailed manakins form leks, groups of 10 to 12 birds that gather purely to perform courtship displays. They sing a song to attract the attention of a female and if they are successful she will stop and watch the performance from a traditional perch. The two principal players in the show are the alpha male and his buddy. Males can take up to four years to decide which team to join, but when they do form a partnership, it lasts a lifetime. Without having to work to raise the young the males have time on their hands, and they often go through their routine even when there isn't a female present so that by the time they have a female audience they are well rehearsed.

Once they have perfected their moves it's time to try out their performance on the females. The male manakins attract the females' attention by giving the melodious 'toledo' call in unison, with the second syllable sung one-and-a-half tones higher than the other two. The pair may repeat the phrase up to 1,000 times per hour, until a passing female comes in for a closer look. David McDonald, from the University of Wyoming, is a leading expert on manakins, having studied them for nearly twenty years. He found that pairs of males who sang this call in tune got the most visits from females. He uses the analogy of two violins, which make a much richer sound when both are in tune. Female manakins proved to be discerning music critics, preferring the best-matched duet even when there was no noticeable difference to the untrained human ear.

The majority of animals are born already equipped to produce appropriate signals.

If the performance is a success, the alpha male will mate with the female while the beta male accepts his role as an apprentice. Females come back to the same lek sites year after year and usually mate with the same male, so getting a good reputation is all-important. A successful alpha can mate as many as 50 or 60 times a year, while most males don't get the chance to mate at all. Being an apprentice requires a lot of patience – a beta male will take the lead role only when the alpha dies and may have to wait as long as ten years before he has his chance at romance.

This kind of lengthy training is very rare in the animal world, so how do most animals know what signals they should produce or how to respond appropriately to those given by others? In general, animals are not conscious of using and responding to the right signals; rather, they are shaped by natural selection to act in certain ways.

With the exception of just a few cases (such as in the development of birdsong), the vast majority of animals come into the world already equipped to produce appropriate signals and no learning is required. This has been clearly demonstrated in studies of crickets which produce sounds by stridulation (Chap 2, p.38), by raising their forewings and rubbing the bases together. It is only

Male crickets are pre-programmed to produce the distinctive song of their species. The sound is made by rubbing their forewings together.

males that stridulate and one of the sounds they make is a species-specific call to attract females. Even if a male cricket is raised in isolation from other crickets, he can still produce this characteristic call and females that have never previously heard any calls seem readily to recognise and respond to their own species call. Researchers have found that if crickets are exposed to nothing but foreign sounds during their development, including the calls of other species, males still develop the right call and females still show a preference for these over anything else. Moreover, males that were a hybrid of two species gave calls that were intermediate between the two parent species, though some attributes of the call were always inherited from the father. For crickets, then, the production and response to signals is genetically fixed.

It comes as no great surprise that a cricket doesn't have to learn his calls. In the same way, an ant doesn't have to experiment with pheromones to see what chemical cocktail is effective for summoning the rest of the troops, nor does a fiddler crab have to discover that waving its claw is a good way of attracting a female. They are pre-programmed to give the right signals – but what of animals that we think of as more intelligent?

Studies have shown that even primates develop their calls instinctively. If squirrel monkeys are reared in isolation from others of their kind, they still develop contact 'peeps' very similar to those of wild monkeys, and these remain virtually unchanged from the first day of life. It seems like a strong argument for nature

A family of pygmy marmosets. Young marmosets produce a jumble of calls called the 'babbling' phase before learning the correct vocabulary.

over nurture, but recent findings makes this less clear-cut. Young monkeys are equipped right from birth to produce the right calls but that doesn't mean they automatically know when to use them or how to respond to them appropriately. This often takes a bit of practice.

Pygmy marmosets babble before they get the hang of their trills. Primatologists Charles Snowdon and A. Margaret Elowson at the University of Wisconsin-Madison studied the development of these marmosets' calls over the first three years of life. The pygmy marmoset (*Cebuella pygmaea*) is the smallest living monkey, a tiny primate no bigger than 20 cm long and weighing about 100 grams. Family groups live together along riversides in the upper Amazon, and in the seasonally flooded forests where they gouge into trees for gum to eat and to catch insects. For the first two weeks of life the young are carried around the forest by their fathers or older siblings. After that they can travel independently but they don't reach maturity for another two years. During their early infancy, the marmosets use a jumble of different trills in a wide variety of contexts. For example, J-calls (a series of particular notes) are typically used by adults that have become separated from their group, but the infants inserted J-calls into calling bouts even when in close proximity to other family members. Snowdon referred to this as the 'babbling' phase, where infants jumble together a wide variety of call types in extensive vocal bouts. Over time, this jumble of trills is gradually refined until the right trill is given in the right context. There is a similar finding in human children, with great variation of producing sounds, words, phrases and grammatical sentences during childhood, but general convergence on competent speech as adults.

Snowdon and Elowson found that adult care-givers were more likely to approach, permit contact with, and groom an infant when the infant was calling than when it was not, so that parental input may be effective simply by encouraging infants to vocalise more often, leading indirectly to appropriate vocalisations.

Vervet monkeys (*Cercopithecus aethiops*) in East Africa give a variety of alarm calls which refer to different types of predator (Chap 2, p.68). Different escape strategies are necessary depending on the danger at hand, and knowing how to differentiate a leopard alarm call from that of an eagle or snake is essential if vervets are to avoid being eaten.

Infant vervets give alarm calls that are acoustically the same as adult alarm calls but that doesn't mean they always get it right. While adult monkeys only give leopard alarms to leopards and cheetahs, eagle alarms to martial or crowned eagles, and snake alarms to pythons and mambas, juveniles will give alarm calls to a much wider variety of species, including animals who pose no threat at all, such as warthogs and even pigeons. On a couple of occasions the group must have been very perplexed when an infant gave an eagle alarm to what turned out to be nothing more dangerous than a falling leaf.

It is interesting, though, that even when infants get it wrong their calls are not completely arbitrary – leopard alarms are given mostly to terrestrial animals, eagle alarms to birds and snake alarms to snakes and lizards. This suggests they are predisposed to divide

A vervet monkey raises the alarm. Infant vervets have to learn to associate different alarm calls with different types of predator.

OPPOSITE | Some types of call appear to produce an instinctive reaction even in very young primates such as this young squirrel monkey.

other species into classes. The categories become more refined with age so that juveniles are a little more selective: they may give an eagle alarm to a goshawk, which is too small to be any threat, but the juveniles have already made a distinction between raptors and non-raptors.

So how do infants come to recognise the correct association between a call and a predator? There is no evidence that they are in any way actively taught when to use alarm calls by adults or chastised if they make mistakes. None the less the social environment is probably very important in the learning process. Adult vervet monkeys take all alarm calls seriously and respond equally to calls given by adults, juveniles, and infants. If an infant is the first to give an eagle alarm, and it is simply a harmless bird, the adults will continue with what they were doing. If, however, the infant was right and there is a martial eagle cruising overhead, the adults will themselves immediately take up the calls. These second alarm calls may then act as a reinforcer, guiding the infants' recognition of the connection between an alarm call and a particular predator.

Learning from adults may also be important when infants are developing and fine-turning responses to different alarm calls. Seyfarth and Cheney played recordings of different alarm calls to youngsters and filmed their responses, which they divided into three categories: 'run to mother', appropriate 'adult-like' responses and 'wrong' responses. Infants between three and four months old typically ran straight to their mothers. Between four and six months, some infants showed adult-like responses but many did completely the wrong thing, like running up to the top of a tree on hearing an eagle alarm or descending into the undergrowth if the alarm signalled a leopard. After six months, it was rare for infants to run to their mothers, few gave the wrong responses and most acted like adults. The researchers were able to see that those who got it right had tended to refer to a nearby adult before taking action and those who responded on their own were more likely to get it wrong. This doesn't prove that vervet monkeys need the example of adults to understand the call, but it does indicate that taking advantage of nearby cues can be very helpful.

The more we learn of primates, the more it appears that proper communication skills are shaped by their social environment. In fact, there are some parallels with the way in which human babies first learn to speak. Babies start to babble spontaneously at about seven months, producing repetitive syllables such as 'ma . . . ma . . . ma' and 'ba . . . ba . . . ba' (which is why the words for mother, father, sister etc. have these elements in so

many languages). At first these syllables are used indiscriminately but gradually, because the baby receives feedback from its social environment, they crystallise into words which relate to specific things, people or situations. For example, if a baby makes a sound that resembles milk it is likely to be given a bottle, which acts as a positive reinforcement. Without social interaction, a baby will not learn to use particular sounds and will gradually stop producing syllables. However, there is a key difference in the learning process of humans and other primates. As humans, we actively teach our young, pointing out the names for things in the environment, and in this it seems we are unique.

BIRDSONG AND DIALECTS

Birdsong has inspired generations of poets, philosophers and naturalists and it is truly remarkable – the winter wren sings 740 notes a minute, the male sedge warbler improvises as he goes along like a jazz singer, never singing the same song twice, while one of the most delightful of minstrels is the nightingale, who may have as many as three hundred love songs in his repertoire. Oscines, or songbirds, produce signals that are so staggeringly complicated that it is hard to imagine how they ever master them.

As early as 1803, Immanuel Kant raised some house sparrows and discovered that their song is not instinctive, but must be learned. The way in which birds do this varies from species to species but there are some underlying rules. Come spring, the song of the chaffinch can be heard in hedgerows, copses and gardens across Europe, Central Asia and North Africa. Every male sings a sweet short song to proclaim his territory, starting with a trill which comprises several phrases and ends with a flourish of 'choo-ee-o'. The song deters other males from encroaching on his patch and attracts passing females. During a season he may sing his song half a million times! If he attracts a mate, she will build a nest and the pair will raise a single brood of four or five chicks which hatch after nearly two weeks of incubation. At the end of the breeding season the pair go their separate ways, males and females often joining separate sex flocks or forming mixed flocks with other finches. The following spring they are both back in their breeding territories, often re-pairing with each other, but this time their offspring are also hoping to breed. Young males born the previous year have to sing their songs in order to establish their territories for the first time. But how do they know what to sing? Hand-reared chicks which are deprived of any contact with parents or other adults still start to sing. This suggests that they are pre-programmed, but the song is very rudimentary – it is the right length and frequency range, but lacks detailed structure.

Amazingly, the chicks are listening to, and learning, their song from the moment they hatch. They don't have long. By August – when the chicks are no more than three months old – the adults will have stopped singing and the chicks will not have another opportunity to learn before they themselves are ready to perform the following spring. By rearing birds and exposing them to recorded songs at different stages, researchers found that there were two critical periods for learning: one straight after hatching and the other the following spring, coinciding with times when they would normally hear the song in the wild. In between, the chicks don't learn even if they are exposed to the song.

During a season the male chaffinch may sing his song half a million times.

These studies led one of the most distinguished researchers in this field, Peter Marler from the University of California in Davis, to put forward the 'auditory template model' of song learning. He suggests that young birds have an in-built rough template defining the general characteristics of their own song. During the first sensitive phase for learning, the chicks also hear the songs of many other birds, but memorise only songs which match this template. This prevents them from picking up an inappropriate song, like a nightingale learning that of a blackbird or wren. Through listening to their father and other males in the vicinity singing, the crude template gradually becomes refined until it provides precise specifications for the song. The following year young males try to match their output to this template. A few rehearsals are usually required and the male first goes through a period of subsong. This is highly variable, as if he were testing out different notes, and he tends to sing rather quietly, as if a little self-conscious of his attempts. Next he graduates to plastic song, so called because it is still quite flexible though louder and more normal in structure,

Female cowbirds may lay as many as forty eggs a year in nests belonging to different species.

and finally the singing crystallises into full song, typical of the adult males of his species.

The exact pattern of song learning differs between species, but in all cases there appears to be an intricate interplay between innate knowledge and learning during periods of sensitivity. Some birds need only to hear their song during the sensitive period and they will pick it up; others, however, are a little more fussy about their education and will only learn from tutors they can interact with. Zebra finches (*Taeniopygia guttafa*), for instance, fail to learn their song altogether if their tutor is a tape-recording, or even a live tutor whom they can hear through a radio link but not see on the other side of an opaque partition. Another experiment found that even if they could see a live tutor through a transparent partition and hear their song, they would still not learn the song if their tutor couldn't hear them. However, if the young birds are blindfolded but can interact with their tutor in the same cage they readily learn their song. Interaction, then, seems to be the key.

These experiments prove that the social environment is critical for young birds to learn their songs. So what happens if a bird not only has no parents but is raised by adults of different species? One such bird is the brown-headed cowbird. It lives in North America and is a brood parasite. That is, female brown-headed cowbirds lay their eggs in other birds' nests and fool them into raising their young. It's a very successful strategy – each female may deposit as many as forty eggs a year in nests belonging to a hundred different species whose eggs are smaller than their own, including song sparrows, yellow warblers, common yellowthroats, Eastern phoebes and Eastern towhees. The female chooses an observation post from which she patiently watches a potential nest. As soon as she sees her intended surrogate starting to lay her eggs, the cowbird sneaks in at dawn and quickly lays a single egg of her own. Occasionally the host may try and push the offensive egg out of the nest but most of the time the cowbird gets away with it. The babies are left in the care of an unwitting babysitter, freeing the parents to follow the meanderings of the buffalo herds, cleaning them of ticks and feasting on the insects stirred up by the constantly moving animals.

The chick of a brown-headed cowbird is raised by a stranger, in this case a yellow warbler, and never has the opportunity to learn its song from its own parents.

Unlike the parasitic cuckoo, young cowbird chicks do not evict their nest-mates when they hatch. But as they usually hatch first and so have the advantage of being larger, they easily out-compete the other chicks. In these circumstances, growing males never have the opportunity to hear their own song.

The young birds leave their nest and head for wintering grounds in the south-eastern United States. Early the following spring they migrate north again to breed and are among the last to arrive. Males select a 'singing tree' from which to sing their song, which typically begins with two liquid whistles and ends in a rapid glissando, sometimes written as 'bub-blow com seee'.

How do the immature male cowbirds know what to sing, having never heard the song before? The answer, it seems, is that they too are born with a rough template, but rather than listening to other males singing to perfect their tune, they try out several versions and rely on the females to tell them which they like best. Evidence for this comes from an experiment involving the two different subspecies of cowbirds, each of which sings its own song.

Young males which were kept in the company of females belonging to the other subspecies developed the song of that subspecies rather than their own. It also transpired that when males sing, females sometimes do a little display called 'wing-stroking' in which they move their wings rapidly back and forth away from their body. This appears to be a sign of approval, because males are far more likely to repeat those songs which elicit wing-stroking from their female companions. Adult males outnumber females by three to two so there is heavy competition.

When birds mature, even more complicated learning can be detected. In many species, males can vary their songs in individual ways without losing their species identity. These variations, which develop when the song is being learned and the male is establishing a territory, are called 'repertoires' and can range from two to several thousand. Some researchers have suggested that birds that can drew on a larger repertoire have an easier time settling into a new territory because they are better able to match the song of a potential neighbour. Another reason why males develop wide repertoires could be to impress females. In many species, females seem to prefer males with extensive song repertoires because it indicates that they are older and more experienced. Finally, developing large repertoires may be useful for defending large territories. This proposition was put forward by John Krebs at Oxford University and called the 'Beau Geste' Hypothesis after P. C. Wren's book about a young soldier of this name who single-handedly defended a fort by propping up his fallen comrades on the battlements, making his enemy think they were meeting a strong force. If a bird constantly rephrases his song and changes his singing perch, he may fool other birds into thinking there are several of him and that the territory is both full and well-defended. Of course this is a ruse that could also deceive potential mates, so male and female birds within an area learn 'dialects'. These are recognisable similarities in birdsong repertories. It appears that although females don't sing, they have a preference for birds with their own dialects.

Regional dialects may develop as a result of juveniles making slight errors in copying adult birds' songs. These errors are then passed down to the next generation in that area, creating the local version which itself will gradually change over time through the same process. However, in a few species songs change so quickly that even over a period of a couple of years the local melody can be quite different. One such African bird is the village indigobird (*Vidua chalybeata*). Like the brown-headed cowbird, the indigobird is a brood parasite. Small groups of males join forces to attract females, singing together in special display areas. Each male in the group may have a repertoire of as many as twenty different songs which are shared by all its members. During the course of the season, a male may change one of the songs slightly and, if one or more of his gang adopt the changes, this will become the new version in subsequent years. Why are the new versions put forward by some males more popular than those suggested by others? A new bit of slang may have intrinsic appeal but it's most likely to stick if used by the 'in crowd'. In the case of the village indigobird, it seems that mating success is the passport to popularity and other males are most likely to copy the male that's best at attracting females.

If a bird constantly rephrases his song and changes his singing perch, he may fool other birds into thinking there are several of him.

FLEXIBILITY AND INTELLIGENCE

When walking through the forests of south-eastern Australia you might hear the harsh cry of a raven, the steady chime of the bellbird, the melodic whistling of an Eastern whipbird, or the crazed laughing of a kookaburra. As the forest is not particularly dense, there is a good chance that you might see one of these birds – except that they may not be there at all. On closer approach, the sight that greets you is a small, innocent-looking brown bird. This is the superb lyrebird (*Menura superba*), who looks much like a long-legged bantam chicken except for the magnificent tail which gives him his name.

Shaking out lacy plumes, he gives an extraordinary cascade of trills, liquid notes and warbles. By borrowing material from other birds, the lyrebird increases the length and variety of his song in a bid to outdo rivals. He does such good cover versions of these songs that very often the original artists themselves are fooled into thinking they have a rival at hand. The lyrebird may include the

The superb lyrebird uses his magnificent tail, arching it over his head to attract a female, as well as a rich vocabulary of borrowed songs and other sounds.

songs of as many as twenty different birds, but this master of mimicry doesn't stop at that – he may include the wingbeats of rosella parrots and, if living close to human habitation, incorporate accurate imitations of dogs barking, car alarms, camera motor drives and even a disconcertingly convincing impression of a chain-saw. One would think all this might be a bit confusing for the female: she may wonder whether she is pairing with a lyrebird, a kookaburra or a lumberjack. However, it seems that the male's visual display is enough to convince her that he is her type and the sound may simply convince her of his talents.

The ability of some birds to mimic a wide variety of sounds may originate from the way in which birds learn their songs. In a number of species, young birds incorporate alien sounds and snatches of other birds' songs in their subsong but by the time they develop true song all these miscellaneous bits have been omitted. Normally it is only young birds that are able to mimic, after which it is hard for them to learn new material, but in a few cases an astonishing ability to mimic continues throughout adult life.

Mockingbirds are so called because they are adept at copying the sounds of other birds. Studies in North America have found that males who are best at pilfering other species' material to create the widest repertoires not only attract females first but also intimidate their fellow males with their musical panache. Starlings (*Sturnus vulgaris*) are also great impersonators; in fact in many parts of North America they readily mock mockingbirds and are capable of causing a certain amount of confusion among humans too. In England there is a story of a starling bringing a football match to an abrupt halt by imitating a referee's whistle and there are also unsettling accounts of starlings imitating V1 flying bombs, or doodlebugs, in London at the end of the Second World War. More recently, there have been reports of starlings doing very good impressions of different mobile-phone ringing tones and even the rather bizarre sounds of modems connecting to the Internet.

This kind of 'cultural evolution' in animal communication is fairly rare but it gives us a fascinating insight into animals' ability to adapt and modify their behaviour, often a mark of intelligence. Now there is evidence that both whales and dolphins also have remarkable powers of mimicry. Dolphins change their whistles to match those of their allies (Chap 2, p.49), while humpback whales can so suddenly and radically alter their songs that it has been described not so much as 'cultural evolution' but 'cultural *revolution*'.

Mike Noad is a marine biologist at the University of Sydney who has been listening to the songs of humpbacks that breed around the Great Barrier Reef, off the east coast of Australia, since 1995. All the males in a given population sing basically the same song, which only changes very gradually over many years as new motifs are added and old ones dropped (Chap 2, p.50). So, when listening to the whales the following year, he was not greatly surprised to hear that the song had changed very slightly. But then, to Noad's amazement, he discovered that two of the 82 whales were singing a totally different song. He got an even bigger surprise when he lowered his hydrophone into the water the year after and found that many of the whales had now adopted the strange new song which, he learned, was almost identical to the song of whales in the Indian Ocean, on the west coast of Australia. He deduced that a few whales from the Indian Ocean population had wandered off course and found themselves in the Pacific, bringing with them a song which was almost an instant hit. By 1998, all 82 males were singing it. Rather than the strangers adopting the local song, the locals opted for the strangers' song. There is no way the males could assess the effectiveness of the new song in attracting available females, as males would have to compare their success with other males over hundreds of thousands of square kilometres of ocean in a relatively short period. So maybe the answer is that these whales simply like singing the latest song.

The ability to learn new material and adapt behaviour in different circumstances can be a considerable advantage to animals. Among a population of ravens in Maine, Bernd Heinrich from the University of Vermont, who has studied them since 1984, found that some learned to use high-pitched shrieking yells to their advantage when finding the remains of a moose or other carrion of ravens. But why should ravens want to attract competitors in this way? By testing various hypotheses, Heinrich came up with the answer. Adult ravens with territories never yell and normally drive away younger ravens from food. Only non-territorial, youthful intruders yell, attracting others of the same status to a food bonanza. By ganging up on the older resident pair they can easily overwhelm their defences. Thus we can conclude that through time, as raven populations boomed and food became a scarce commodity, especially in winter, the yell signal has been adopted by young, landless ravens to outnumber older mated pairs at desirable food sites.

OPPOSITE | A humpback whale launches its forty tonne body out of the water – this extraordinary behaviour is likely to be some form of display, but may also be used to stun fish.

Are these changes in the use of signals just random and accidental or do they suggest underlying intelligence? Any direct knowledge of how an animal experiences its world is impossible to acquire and the only way we can ever get a glimpse into the mind of an animal – or another human being for that matter – is through their outward expressions.

The reason parrots have such an outstanding talent for mimicry remains a mystery.

In an experiment Alex carefully counts 'Two . . . three . . . four . . . five . . . sih.' The x in six is a difficult sound for Alex to make because he is a parrot. A 22-year-old African grey, Alex has been the subject of long-term research by Irene Pepperburg at the University of Arizona. He has learned over seven hundred words – a vocabulary comparable to that of an average eight-year-old child. In early attempts to teach parrots to speak, they got no further than most household pets in their communicative abilities, but Pepperburg has employed an altogether different technique which has provided some extraordinary results. In a typical training session, Alex works with two people, a trainer and a student. The trainer directs a question at the student, who acts as both a model for Alex and as a rival for the trainer's attention. The roles of trainer and student are regularly reversed so that Alex understands that communication is a two-way business and that each vocalisation is not specific to an individual. While trainer and student play the question-and-answer game, Alex can't help but butt in with the answers first. These are not just random chatterings; he can name and describe as many as a hundred different objects with 80 per cent accuracy, saying what colour they are, what material, and what shape.

Pepperburg describes how, in addition to understanding that colours and shapes represent different categories and that objects can be grouped accordingly, Alex seems to grasp the idea that a single object can possess attributes of more than one category. For example, a green triangle is both green and three-cornered and if Alex is presented with one and asked 'What shape?' or 'What colour?' he can change his basis for classification according to the question and give the correct answer. Moreover, Alex seems to comprehend the concept of 'same' and 'different'. If shown two identical objects which differ in only one respect, say two wooden triangles, one blue and the other green, and asked 'What is the same?' Alex will answer 'Matter' or 'Shape', suggesting that he is indeed listening to the question, rather than responding to prior training in which case he would be likely to pick out what was obviously different – colour. Alex can examine a tray of seven different objects and respond accurately to questions such as 'What colour is the block?', 'What object is red?', 'What shape is the wood?', 'How many keys are there?'

He has also learned to say phrases and sentences, often in masterful performances. Once, when Pepperburg took him to the vet for lung surgery and she turned to leave him, Alex called out, 'Come here. I love you. I'm sorry. I want to go back.'

There is no evidence that parrots use their extraordinary powers of impersonation in the wild, and the reason why they have such an astounding talent for mimicry remains a mystery. But what of parrots' intelligence? Alex certainly seems to know what he is talking about, or does he? Some researchers dispute the validity of the research, but the results are so astonishing that they cannot be dismissed out of hand. Alex seems to be performing on a cognitive level akin to dolphins, chimpanzees and young children. Even if he is half as intelligent as he appears, it throws the whole question of intelligence wide open – parrots have very little grey matter and thus not much of a cerebral cortex, the brain region associated with cognitive processing in higher mammals.

However, there is one thing that parrots, dolphins, chimpanzees and humans all have in common: they live in close-knit groups with a changing membership. In these societies, relationships are less predictable and the individual has to be ready to adapt to different situations. Gradually we may come to a better understanding of what is going on in Alex's head. Perhaps the level of cognitive processing is not what it appears to be. Alternatively, maybe many animals actually have a greater intelligence than we give them credit for and than our methods of evaluation have yet enabled us to discover.

The strident alarm calls of the go-away-bird are heeded by many animals in the African bush.

TALKING A FOREIGN LANGUAGE

It's about -30°C and in every direction a vast white canvas of snow stretches as far as the eye can see. Over the brow of the ridge a team of shaggy huskies hurtles into view pulling a sled, a cloud of white billowing behind them. At the controls, the musher's face is barely visible behind the thick fur of his hood but his calls ring out clearly in the crisp air, puffs of smoke escaping from his mouth as he shouts 'gee' and 'haw'. The dog team responds to his directions instantly, moving to the right or left in perfect unison to avoid the pitfalls hidden deep under the Alaskan snow. It is one of the most extraordinary sights, not only for its wild beauty but for its portrayal of such apparent understanding between two completely different creatures.

Many people talk to their pets and swear that they are understood. In the case of people and dogs the relationship goes back at least 14,000 years and so it is not surprising that we have learned the knack of interpreting each other's signals. Just as dogs and humans have shared the same environment for countless generations, many other animals have long been neighbours with other species and can often 'understand' and take advantage of their signals.

Taking advantage of each other's warning signals is of course an especially good idea if you have the same enemies. In the White Mountains of California, yellow-bellied marmots (*Marmota flaviventris*) and golden-mantled ground squirrels (*Spermophilus lateralis*) share the same environment and, despite their difference in size, are both at risk from coyotes and golden eagles. They react with equal consternation on hearing their own or each other's alarm calls, either taking refuge or standing upright and scanning the area, but they take no notice of each other's non-alarm calls. In many parts of Africa, hunters' attempts at stalking prey can be thwarted by the distinctive bleating calls of the grey go-away-bird (*Corythaixoides concolor*) which alerts everyone in the vicinity to the presence of danger. I recall walking quietly through the scrubby bush in Zimbabwe once, hoping to encounter animals but finding instead a go-away-bird, a grey-coloured bird with pronounced crest and long tail who dogged me in the most frustrating manner, fluttering alongside me from bush to bush calling persistently at the top of its voice. Needless to say I saw nothing on my walk except for my excitable companion! In other circumstances, animals' alarm signals can be very useful to humans. Chris Watson, a sound recordist who has worked on several occasions in Kenya's Masai Mara, told me how they would often listen for the alarm calls of vervet monkeys (p.211) when trying to find leopards or cheetahs in the area.

The relationship between people and dogs goes back at least 14,000 years.

Although the vervet monkeys have their own alarm calls, they've gone one better and learned to recognise and respond to the calls of birds, too. In Amboseli National Park in Kenya vervet monkeys live alongside a brightly coloured songbird, the superb starling (*Spreo superbus*). Like vervet monkeys, these starlings have different alarm calls for different predators – a raspy chatter in response to a terrestrial predator and a clear undulating whistle in response to hawks or eagles. If the starlings emit a harsh chattering cry, the vervets take to the trees, but a clear whistle makes them look up to the sky. Marc Hauser, a researcher working in Amboseli, found that different groups of vervets living in different habitats, with different numbers of starlings, encountered and heard the starlings' warning calls at different rates. For example, vervets in residence by the swamps heard the calls every fifteen minutes or so, whereas those living in dry woodland areas heard them about half as often. Hauser decided to find out whether this exposure affected how infants learned to recognise the calls of starlings. He played back the calls to vervet monkeys of different ages in the two groups and found that those who lived by the swamp reacted to the calls at a much earlier age than those in the woodland, showing that experience can be just as important when learning to recognise the call of another species as it is for many animals when learning the meanings of their own calls.

In the same way that different species can listen in on each other's alarm signals to warn them of danger, animals may eavesdrop on each other's food calls to learn about good places to eat. Insectivorous bats use echolocation to find their prey, such as moths, in complete darkness, but they have to be quick because their ultrasonic sounds will alert other bats to the potential snack in the area. In certain cases, the caller receives clear benefits from attracting individuals with its food calls. For instance, in some social feeding birds such as domestic chickens, males provide food calls that attract potential mates. In many primate groups, individuals call to attract other members of their group to share a food discovery which is likely to be reciprocated at a later date. And finally, attracting other individuals to a location can reduce the risk of predation since it increases the number of other potential victims. So it seems that in many cases callers have exploited the eavesdropping tactics of other members of their species for their own benefit.

Offering food to another individual is such a universally understood gesture of friendship that it easily transcends the species barrier.

Being able to 'understand' what other species say can obviously be very useful but so, too, can impersonating them. By mimicking the sounds of snakes, Southern black tits (*Parus niger*) manage to make themselves appear far more dangerous than they are. They nest in natural tree-holes in the savannah woodlands of southern Africa, where they are vulnerable to both owls and snakes. If they sense any disturbance at the mouth of their hole they take advantage of the shroud of darkness and hiss like a snake, which is usually enough to give the predator second thoughts.

If you are going to mimic another species in order to secure your own safety, then one of the most effective ploys would be to imitate humans who are feared by even the top predators in most parts of the world. Indeed, there is a remarkable account from Africa of a fork-tailed drongo (*Dicrurus adsimilis*) which learned to whistle like a shepherd so as to deceive local birds of prey into staying out of the area.

One great advantage in learning to imitate another species is that you can use their signals to persuade them to come to your aid. The well-known American ornithologist Eugene Morton cast himself in the role of a predator and approached the nest of a thick-billed euphonia (*Euphonia laniirostris*) to see how it would react. On sensing danger the adult bird did not give its own nest alarm call, but instead gave the mobbing calls of other local birds such as tanagers (family Thraupidae) and honeycreepers (family Coerebidae), thus inciting them into taking action and driving Morton away, while the euphonia itself remained hidden at a safe distance. And if you can gather a defence force by using the alarm signals of another species, so can you send them away by imitating their repelling calls. It seems that the African chorister robin chat (*Cossypha dichroa*) uses its flair for imitation to do just that. By singing the songs of competing species, it apparently fools members of those species into thinking that territories are occupied and making them go elsewhere.

Ants are rewarded with sweet droplets from the caterpillar of a gossamer-winged butterfly, in return for protecting it against spiders and parasitic wasps.

Sometimes, however, animals learn each other's codes in order to genuinely co-operate. Offering food to another individual is such a universally understood gesture of friendship that it easily transcends the species barrier. Many species of gossamer-winged butterflies (Lycaenidae) form close associations with ants during their caterpillar stage. The caterpillars feed on nitrogen-fixing plants such as lupin and then secrete droplets rich in sugars and amino acids from a specialised gland. This nutritious delicacy is traded with the ants for protection against their enemies: spiders and parasitic wasps. If the caterpillar senses danger, it immediately waves its tentacles and ants hurry into action, forming a barricade around it. As the number of ants in attendance increases, the tentacle display becomes less frequent and it may be that in this way the caterpillar balances its need for protection against the amount of food it must produce. It is thought that the substances released from the tentacles are mimics of ant pheromones, but the ants aren't simply being fooled into acting as bodyguards; they too are carefully reading the signals and responding accordingly – the greater the tentacle-waving, the better the supper.

Some animals have abilities that others lack and by joining forces they can achieve something that would have been very difficult alone. Perhaps there is no wild creature that is more adept at getting assistance from another species than the honeyguide. Both the greater, or black-throated, honeyguide (*Indicator indicator*) and the scaly-throated honeyguide (*I. variegatus*) are small birds with exacting tastes. They like beeswax and bee larvae, but the hives of the wild bees are mini-fortresses built up in high trees or protected in rock crevices and termite mounds. For a bird less than 20 cm long, getting through the tough walls of a beehive and avoiding being stung to death is no easy feat. It is better to call on help, and the best option is to find a honey badger or ratel (*Mellivora capensis*) which is perfectly equipped for the job. It can climb, has large claws and an inbuilt immobilising spray and, furthermore, is very partial to honey. On finding its friend, the honeyguide flies around giving a series of repetitive chirring notes, fanning its tail and arching and ruffling its wings to expose yellow shoulder bands. Once it has the badger's attention, the honeyguide leads the way back to the beehive it has discovered, alighting at regular intervals and giving a persistent 'tirr-tirr-tirr-tirr' while it waits for the badger to catch up. On arrival, the badger climbs up to the hive and tears it apart with its large claws, its paws protected from any bee attack by thick leathery skin. In addition, the badger releases a special noxious fluid from its anal glands which drives off the bees and immobilises any who don't make a quick enough

OPPOSITE CLOCKWISE FROM TOP LEFT | The honey guide is good at locating honey but needs to enlist help from a ratel – or human – to break open a tough beehive.

The ratel, or honey badger, works in partnership with the honey guide. When the bird has located a beehive the badger has no problem gaining access.

Large claws and strong jaws enable a ratel to break open a beehive.

getaway. The badger and the honeyguide then both dine on the spoils – the badger munching honeycomb while the bird feasts on bee larvae and wax.

If the honeyguide can't find a badger it will find the next best alternative: a human. Researchers have studied the relationship between the Boran people of northern Kenya and the honeyguides. Honey is an important part of the Boran's diet and the honeyguides' assistance in finding hives is most welcome – on average, searching for beehives took an unaided human some 8.9 hours, but with the help of the honeyguide that was reduced to just 3.2 hours. A special relationship has been forged between the two species, who exchange signals in order to co-operate. The Boran people produce a penetrating whistle by blowing air into clasped fists or instruments such as snail shells or hollowed-out doum palm nuts. This sound carries through the acacia woodlands for more than a kilometre and calls the birds to join the expedition. If the honeyguide has found a hive, it flies close to the honey gatherer, moving restlessly between perches while giving the double-noted 'tirr tirr . . . tirr'. Then it flies off through the treetops displaying its white outer tail feathers and disappears for some minutes before returning and perching conspicuously. As soon as the Boran gets close it flies off to another perch about 50 metres away, calling insistently, and so on until they reach the hive.

Wearing camouflage allows predators to get close to unsuspecting prey, but another way to sneak up on a target without arousing suspicion is to change your behaviour.

The Boran people claim that, from the honeyguides' flight pattern, perching height and calls, they can work out not only the direction of the hive but the distance as well. The longer the bird disappears on the first encounter, the further away the site is thought to be; also the distance between perches is greater and the perches are higher when the hive is some way off. It is an extraordinary example of co-operation and understanding between people and wild animals.

Being able to talk across the species barrier can bring enormous benefits. Not only might you induce another animal to assist you in getting at food, you might even persuade it to take care of you altogether. Though we tend to think that we have domesticated certain animals for our own benefit, the alternative is that certain animals have adopted us – a theory that has its roots in the self-domestication of the wolf, seeking food and shelter. Whoever made the first approach, it was only by being able to read each other's signals that man and animal could have developed such a close, mutually beneficial relationship.

WHY TELL THE TRUTH?

Animals of different species spend a lot of time trying to outwit each other. This is especially true of predators and their prey, and in the game of cat-and-mouse cheating is not out of order. Predators on the prowl use lots of sly tricks to catch their victims and one of the best is to adopt a disguise. Many predators develop perfect camouflage: snakes are frequently beautifully patterned to melt away in the grass or leaf litter, some fish take on the appearance of rocks, while the masters of concealment are chameleons who can continually alter their appearance to suit their surroundings. Wearing camouflage allows predators to get close to unsuspecting prey, but another way to sneak up on a target without arousing suspicion is to change your behaviour.

Merlins (*Falco columbarius*) try to blend in with the scene by mimicking the undulating flight of a harmless woodpecker or pigeon. Their prey, which include finches, sparrows and cardinals as well as small mammals, lizards and frogs, are lulled into a false sense of security when they see a 'pigeon' flying overhead but at the last minute the merlin suddenly unmasks itself, rising up and diving headlong at its victim. Similarly the zone-tailed hawk (*Buteo albonotatus*) plays the part of a turkey vulture (*Cathartes aura*) in order to get close to its prey. Turkey vultures eat only carrion, not live prey, so animals on the ground don't regard them as a threat and go about their business as usual. The hawk imitates the vultures' flight and underwing markings, but it goes one step further and uses them as cover, circling high on thermals among a spiral of vultures so that it can get a fix on its target without being spotted.

Other predators take on a more active role in laying a trap. One of the most remarkable methods of luring an animal to its death is practised by the slaty-backed forest falcon (*Micrastur mirandollei*) from Panama. It hides itself in dense foliage and gives a ventriloquial series of clear whistles which attracts curious birds.

The falcon then finds it easy to dart from its hiding place and snatch one of the more daring birds who approach to investigate, among them probably some naïve North American migrants unaware of the dangers of the tropical forest.

By producing a substance that closely resembles the intoxicating pheromone of a female moth, this bolus spider lures unsuspecting male moths to their doom.

Imitating other animals' signals is a good way to attract them and there are few signals more alluring than those of a sexually receptive female. The bolus spider (*Mastophora hutchinsoni*) entices hapless male moths into its jaws by imitating female moths. Female bolus spiders exude a special chemical which closely mimics the female sex hormones of two nocturnal species of moth, the bristly cutworm (*Lacinipolia renigera*) and the smoky tetanolita (*Tetanolita mynesalis*). Male moths are drawn by the intoxicating aroma of their females, only to discover their mistake too late. Rather than the female moth they had hoped for, they are confronted by a voracious female spider who strikes them abruptly with a sticky ball of silk (bolus) before devouring them.

Predators do not have it all their own way and sometimes those who are preyed upon can give their enemies quite a surprise. The circular markings on the wings of many moths may make them appear as enormous-eyed monsters and predators may think twice about attacking. In the same way, the false eyespots of butterfly fish are more than six times larger than their real eyes and perhaps deceive would-be attackers into thinking they are tackling a much larger animal. If a predator does decide to strike, the false eyespots may direct its attacks to less vital body areas.

Animals who are not inclined to draw attention to themselves can always use another of the predators' tricks and pretend not to be there at all. The great potoo (*Nyctibius grandis*) is a kind of nightjar that is found in forests from Panama to Brazil. It is nocturnal and by day it must get some rest, but a bird asleep in broad daylight is likely to be vulnerable, so the potoo is adapted to look exactly like a branch. Camouflaged in patchy grey, it flattens itself against the tree-trunks and closes its eyes so that nothing gives it away. Even with this disguise the potoo doesn't feel entirely safe in the forests of the Amazon and so it keeps watch through a tiny spyhole formed by a little hook on its eyelid.

OPPOSITE | Just part of the scenery. This South American potoo sleeps during the day and is a master of disguise.

Some of the best defence strategies don't rely simply on adopt-

A Texas horned lizard blends with its environment while lying in wait for prey.

OPPOSITE | Any predator approaching a Texas horned lizard gets more than it bargained for as the lizard sends jets of blood squirting out of its eyes.

ing the right appearance but on adopting the right attitude too. The prize for best performance goes to the Texas horned lizards (*Phrynosoma cornutum*). These lizards eat ants and other small invertebrates which they search for in open areas, quietly awaiting their prey and then swiftly ambushing it. This feeding behaviour means that the lizard has to wait for long periods out in the open and so is itself vulnerable to a whole host of predators including hawks, roadrunners, snakes, coyotes and ground squirrels as well as domestic dogs and cats. But any predator approaching a horned lizard is in for a big shock. When threatened, it turns from a small, handsome, greyish-brown lizard into an enormous spiny balloon. More alarming still, the walls between its sinuses and eye-sockets burst, sending jets of blood squirting out of its eyes over more than a metre. One theory suggests that this bizarre behaviour is irritating to predators; a second, which seems quite plausible, is that the predator is so surprised that it hesitates and this gives the lizard valuable seconds in which to make good its escape.

Even without such amazing props animals can often fool and confuse others simply by playing very convincing roles which may be acted out to protect not only themselves but their loved ones too. The plover (family Charadriidae) lays its eggs on the ground where they are vulnerable to predators, but despite this plovers are most protective parents. If a fox appears on the scene the plover employs impressive acting skills to deceive it. Moving away from the nest, it takes up a strange attitude, spreading its tail in an abnormal fashion or dragging its wing on the ground so that it appears to be injured. Sometimes the plover gets so engrossed in its role that it falls over and flops about, its wing dragging helplessly. Predators are always alert for any kind of weakness and such an easy meal must be a very tempting prospect. The fox can't help but switch its attention to the parent bird and give chase, and as soon as it has been lured a reasonable distance away from the nest, the plover flies off fit and well and returns to tend its precious clutch.

The nest of the piping plover (*Charadrius melodus*) on the sandy beaches and lake shores in temperate North America is just as exposed, but when an animal approaches, the incubating bird doesn't cower over the eggs. Instead it stands up boldly and walks slowly away from the nest. When it is a few metres away it starts calling, giving a plaintive 'peeping' sound which has earned it its name. Often it will then move towards the predator and attract attention with a conspicuous display. In one such display, called a crouch run, the parent bird stoops close to the ground, lowering its head and running in a way that makes it look like a small rodent such as a vole. Sometimes it even gives little squeaks to accentuate its vole impression. Most of the predators that are after the plover's eggs and chicks are equally fond of eating voles and so are easily tempted away from their original purpose.

Pretending to have a broken wing is a clever ploy used by plovers to lead predators away from their precious eggs.

In the past, scientists were sceptical that a bird could intentionally deceive a predator in order to lead it away from young. Instead, the plover's extraordinary broken-wing performance was explained as the result of internal conflict in the bird, which is motivated both to run and to attack and so is thrown into a state of chaos. But the plover's convincing 'easy target' performance, and its effectiveness in luring foxes away from their nests, suggest that there is more to it than this; moreover, the theory hardly explains the piping plover's pretending to be a vole. One piece of evidence, however, does support the notion that the birds are not conscious of their behaviour: they will sometimes continue with their displays even after the predator has killed its prey.

On the other hand, there is plenty to suggest that the birds are perfectly well aware of what they are doing. During a display, the plover frequently looks at the intruder to gauge its reaction. If the intruder doesn't follow the decoy, the bird typically moves to a more conspicuous position where it resumes its display with increased vigour. Plovers are also selective about which intruders warrant a full-blown display and even about what kind of display is appropriate. On busy beaches they often don't bother displaying if approached by familiar people. If cattle or hoofed animals approach the nest, the danger is not that eggs or chicks will be eaten but that they will be trampled to death; then, rather than appearing to be injured, the parent stands up conspicuously by the nest and spreads its wings to show that it is there. In extremis, it may even fly directly at the approaching cow and force it to change course.

Patterns of behaviour can evolve more rapidly than physical attributes and thus remain more flexible. Along with the physical environment, the living environment of relationships which an animal has both with members of its own kind and with other species is in a constant state of flux. An animal that can adapt quickly – changing its behaviour to deceive or avoid deception, for instance – is better able to cope in adverse circumstances. The fox will starve if it is always fooled by the plover's broken-wing display. And in some places there is evidence that foxes have caught on to the injury scam. Grouse perform a display very similar to plovers when red foxes approach their nests, but Geir Sonerud from the University of Tennessee described how, in the northern boreal zone of south-east Norway, not only did the foxes refuse to fall for it, they had even learned that it was a positive indication of chicks nearby and so actively searched the area. Of course, once the fox gets wind of the deception, the birds must come up with a new ploy if they are to save their young. Judging by relative brain size throughout evolution, animals in general have grown smarter. This may be because an animal pays a price whenever it is duped and so there is a strong selection to avoid being deceived. These dual forces of deception and counter-deception lead to an escalating intellectual arms race that many scientists believe is a major driving force in the evolution of animal intelligence. If, from previous experience, you can second-guess an individual's reaction in any situation and alter your signals accordingly in order to manipulate them, then that intellectual arms race rapidly becomes a sprint.

Being able to outwit another animal is not confined to the

OVER PAGE | A sun bittern can transform itself into a red-eyed monster to intimidate other birds into handing over food.

relationship between predators and their prey, it's about getting the advantage in all kinds of situations. Other elements in the environment can play a part. While predators and prey are locked in a battle for survival, others might be on the sidelines hoping for a free lunch. The mission of the sun bittern (*Eurypyga helias*) is not to catch prey or avoid being eaten, but to steal food from others. In order to make a living as a con artist it is important to be aware of everyone else's business and the bittern sits in reedbeds along rivers in southern Venezuela and watches the world go by. If a hawk spies a lizard and swoops down to grab it, the bittern leaps out of the bushes and transforms itself into a terrifying red-eyed monster. Crouching low, it spreads its wings, revealing enormous rich chestnut eye-spots. The hawk is frequently so taken aback by this sudden apparition that it drops the lizard and takes flight. The bittern then resumes its normal appearance and helps itself to the lizard.

Animal signals are usually truthful because if they are misleading they will eventually be ignored.

Another bird uses a cunning strategy to get rid of competition. Great tits (*Parus major*) give false alarm calls in order to disperse flocks of sparrows which often monopolise a food source. But as with predators and prey, if food is scarce, other birds will have to get wise to the great tits' lies and the great tits will in turn have to come up with a new strategy.

During the winter, or when great tits feed intensively in order to replenish fat stores (in the early morning and evening before going to roost), they will even give alarm calls to frighten other great tits away from desirable food. Dominant great tits will use alarm calls deceptively only if another dominant individual is feeding at a concentrated food source; a subdominant bird is simply chased away with threat displays. This suggests that great tits benefit by economising on their use of false alarm calls: if they are used too frequently, the other birds may catch on and ignore the calls.

THE LANGUAGE OF DECEIT

In a competitive world, keeping one step ahead of the game may be the best way to ensure success. Some of the most intense competition usually comes from members of your own species because you share the same desires. In general, animal signals are truthful because if they are misleading they will eventually be ignored by others, like the boy who cried wolf. Furthermore many cues, such as those related to fighting ability, are costly in terms of energy and are difficult to bluff. Among red deer stags, for instance, deep frequencies and high rates of roaring simply cannot be produced and sustained by smaller, weaker stags (Chap 2, p.58). But if you can deceive your fellows it might be very profitable.

One day in the forests of Gombe National Park in Tanzania I was following a group of male chimpanzees who were particularly excitable, displaying wildly and calling back and forth because one of the females, Gremlin, was sexually receptive. Although the alpha male, Wilkie, was closely guarding Gremlin from the attentions of the other males, the posse hung around the couple, waiting for any chance they could get to mate with her. The group had stopped for a while up the valley and tensions were mounting. This is a time when male chimpanzee politics are at their most feverish. Wilkie had his work cut out to keep an eye on Gremlin while simultaneously dashing about and displaying in an attempt to keep order in the ranks. Eventually some of the males dispersed into the thick vegetation and Wilkie and the female moved down the slope.

With a fellow field researcher, Bill Wallauer, I followed Wilkie, but only moments later, from up the slope, we heard a male called Beethoven give repeated loud 'waa barks', a dramatic call that is often given in defiance when a chimp is attacked. Without hesitating, Wilkie turned abruptly and charged back up the hill to sort out the problem. Then, to our amazement, Beethoven stepped out from the undergrowth completely unruffled. With Wilkie out of sight he shook a branch at Gremlin by way of threat, and then led her helter-skelter down the slope and away. Bill and I scrambled after them and caught up again some distance later. Calls echoed round the forest elsewhere but Beethoven and Gremlin remained steadfastly silent. Of course we can't be sure that Beethoven's intention was to deceive and perhaps he really had been attacked – although, if so, he recovered pretty quickly. But whether by luck or cunning, from a no-win situation Beethoven had ended up with Gremlin.

A robin sings with gusto at dawn.

Among members of highly social species such as chimpanzees there is a delicate balance between pursuing the groups' interests and looking out for your own. On another occasion in Gombe I was following a group of male chimpanzees who were heading out to patrol the southern boundary of their range to stop incursions by neighbouring chimpanzees. Such missions can be dangerous and the more males the better. En route the chimps stopped to feed in a rich fruit tree just a valley away from the border. After half an hour or so some males climbed down to resume their journey, including the alpha male and another old and experienced male called Goblin. They waited a while at the bottom of the tree but when the others didn't seem inclined to join them they set off again towards the border, with me in tow. As we neared the top of the ridge the males sat down and repeatedly glanced back the way we had come, as if waiting for a sign that the others were following. After about five minutes, Goblin started to give loud food 'pant hoots' which were immediately taken up by the others, along with a medley of excited food grunts. I was bewildered – there didn't seem to be a good food supply anywhere close by. Within minutes the stragglers showed up and without further ado Goblin and the others set off at a good pace, leading the whole party over the ridge and down to the border.

It is difficult to be certain that we have evidence for deception within species because we can't guarantee that the animals' signals don't mean something else. Although I have never heard chimpanzees give those calls in any context other than feeding or approaching food, I cannot be absolutely sure that they do not mean 'Get over here' rather than 'Food!' None the less, the behaviour shown by the chimps on these occasions was unique. Whereas the plover's broken-wing display and the other examples of deception discussed in the last section are regularly and widely used patterns of behaviour, the instances of apparent deception in chimpanzees were spontaneous, implying the ability of one animal to read another's mind on the spur of the moment, to empathise, if you will.

If, once the meanings of signals are established, you can get one over on your fellows by lying, it requires others to evaluate information more carefully.

Human language is by far the most sophisticated communication system we know and for a long time the received wisdom was that it evolved so that we could pass on information in order to co-operate efficiently. But, as we have seen, the interests of the group are not always the same as the interests of the individual and more recently 'Machiavellian intelligence', or the manipulation of others, has been proposed as another force driving the complexity and versatility of language. If, once the meanings of signals are established, you can get one over on your fellows by lying, it requires others to evaluate information more carefully, which bring a significant element of plasticity into communication systems – the kinds of signals used, the contexts they are used in, the interpretation of signals and the response.

But communication, be it human or animal, goes beyond just conveying information or misinformation. Both animals and humans often put a lot more time and energy into communicating than is strictly necessary to get information across. A robin singing at dawn seems to put his heart and soul into his song and repeats it time and time again, chimpanzees engage in prolonged and diligent grooming sessions – an equivalent of our sociable chatting – and young animals, like young humans, energetically repeat the same sounds or gestures to get the desired response from their parents. This extra investment is not redundant when the main purpose is to make an impression, to bond or to persuade. Communication is the way in which all animals co-ordinate behaviour within their own species and connect with the world around them. For us, as a highly social species, this urge to connect is so strong that it crosses the species barrier – we talk to animals, study their cryptic codes and even try to teach them our language. And perhaps this is why the legend of King Solomon's ring, which allowed him to understand and speak the language of animals, will always strike a chord with us.

Acknowledgements

First and foremost I would like to thank the excellent team at BBC's Natural History Unit with whom I made the television series "Talking with Animals". Not only was making the series a great adventure it also gave me the opportunity to write a book on a subject I love. In particular, I am indebted to Bernard Walton, the series producer, to Lizzie Bewick and Scott Alexander who produced two of the programmes and to Sara Ford and Keith Scholey for their valuable suggestions and support. There are many people who have been vital to the success of the project and who have also been a great pleasure to work with and I want to express my warmest thanks to Bridget Appleby, James Brickell, Caroline Marriott, Gaynor Scattergood, Jolie Bradfield, Sally Mark and my favourite diving buddy, Diane Tanner. I was fortunate to work with some very talented film crews, including cameramen Rod Clarke, Mark Yates, Peter Scoones, Richard Kirby, Andrew Penniket, Nick Hayward, Roger Long and David Rasmussen and sound recordists Kevin Meredith, Tim Allen, Chris Taylor and David Parkinson and technical operator Andy Milk, and I would like to thank them all for making it so much fun. And thank you also to Georgette Douwma for taking some wonderful pictures of cuttlefish and dolphins on location. There is one sound recordist, Chris Watson, to whom I would like to say an especially big thank you for his extremely useful insights into the nature of sound, for his enthusiasm in discussing animal communication and, not least, his excellent sense of humour.

The project relied on the support of many dedicated field researchers who gave us the benefit of their expertise while filming. In particular I want to thank Joyce Poole, Steve Insley, Neil Krekorian, Sarah Conditt Humfeld, Andej Cokl and Meta Virant-Doberlet, Max Egan, Gail Patricelli, Steve Alm, Tony Bramley, Sean and Jan Ellis, George Uetz, Marc Dantzker, John Barimo, Cory Miller, Robert Platt, Jochen Zeil, Carol Curtis, Nikolai Hiristov, Peng Lee, Robert Hickling, Chris Boland, Javier Mercado and Con Slobodchikoff for their considerable assistance.

The subject of animal communication is vast and new discoveries are being made at an astounding rate so I am deeply grateful to the many scientists who were kind enough to cast their eye over sections of the manuscript and offer their comments, especially Philip Stoddard of Florida University for his useful suggestions on electric fish, Andrej Cokl of Ljubijana University on stink bugs, Andrew Bass of Cornell University on midshipman fish, Joyce Poole of the Amboseli Elephant Project and Caitlin O'Connell-Rodwell of Stanford University on elephants, Innes Cuthill and Robert Thomas of Bristol University on the dawn chorus, Clive Catchpole at Royal Holloway, University of London for general thoughts on bird song, Maree Elowson and Charles Snowdon of the University of Wisconsin-Madison on pygmy marmosets, David McDonald of Wyoming University on long-tailed manakins, Gail Patricelli of the University of Maryland on bowerbirds, Sarah Conditt Humfeld of the University of Missouri-Columbia on green tree frogs, Jim Morin of Cornell University on ostracods, Justin Marshall of University of Queensland on cleaner fish, Michael Noad of the University of Sydney on humpback whale songs, Allison Alberts of the University of California at San Diego and Neil Krekorian of San Diego State University on desert iguanas and also Stephen Simpson of Oxford University on locusts.

Anyone opening this book will be struck first by the wonderful images and the credit for this goes to Juliet Brightmore at Hodder & Stoughton, who went well beyond the call of duty in sourcing them, particularly those illustrating rare behaviour or obscure animals. I am thrilled with the work ofYan Golunksi of Jelly Telly, whose exciting graphics enable us to envisage the animal senses that we cannot perceive. I am also very grateful to Richard Ranft, the Curator of the Wildlife Section at the British Library National Sound Archive for providing us with bird sonograms and to Jeremy Ashcroft, for his superb work on the graphs. I would also very much like to thank the designers at Hodder & Stoughton, Janette Revill and Alasdair Oliver who have pulled all this together and given the book such an exciting and distinctive look. Finally, thank you to Helen Birkbeck who came in at the last moment to help type up the bibliography.

The patience, understanding and encouragement of all my family and friends helped me tremendously and though I can not name everyone individually here, I really want to say how grateful I am to them all. I especially want to thank my parents for being so supportive throughout and for their valuable comments on the manuscript, to Mike Scott for frequently coming to the rescue when life looked like it might get out of control and to my dear friend Sibylla Wood simply for being who she is. Also to another dear friend, Jem, a border collie, who made sure I got regular walks and though he was not much help discussing the text, was always ready to demonstrate important aspects of dog communication.

I also wish to express my deepest thanks to Sheila Ableman, my agent, for her counsel and friendship, and for helping to make this book happen. More than anyone, it is Rupert Lancaster at Hodder & Stoughton who has brought together all the elements to make this book a success and he has my warmest thanks for being so supportive, calm and wonderful to work with. My very, very special thanks to Caroline Taggart, whose suggestions and assistance in editing the manuscript improved the book immeasurably. And finally, a huge thank you to Caroline Marriott without whom I would not have been able to do it. I am deeply indebted to her for all her enthusiastic and efficient help in researching the book, checking facts and figures, acting as a sounding board for ideas and generally making sure that I did justice to the subject.

Sources and Bibliography

Ackers, S.H., & Slobodchikoff, C N. Communication of stimulus size and shape in alarm calls of Gunnison's prairie dogs. *Ethology* (1999), Vol.105, pp.149-162

Adamo, S.A., & Hanlon, R T. Do cuttlefish (*Cephalopoda*) signal their intentions to conspecifics during agonistic encounters? *Animal Behaviour* (1996), Vol. 52, pp. 73-81

Agosta, W.C. *Chemical Communication: the language of pheromones*, Scientific American Library, New York, 1992

Andrew, R. J. The origin and evolution of the calls and facial expressions of the primates. *Behaviour* (1962), Vol. 20, pp. 1-93

Aubin, T. & Jouventin, P. Cocktail-party effect in king penguin colonies. *Proceedings of the Royal Society, London B*, 265 (1998), pp. 1665-1673

Barth, F.G. *et al.* Spiders of the genus *Cupiennius* Simon 1891 (*Aranaea, Ctenidae*), *Oecologia* 77 (1988), 194-201

Benton, T.G. Courtship behaviour of the scorpion, *Euscorpius flavicaudis*. *Bulletin of the British Arachnological Society*, 9: 5 (1993), 137-141

Baurecht, D. & Barth, F. Vibratory communication in spiders. *Journal of Comparative Physiology A* 171 (1992), pp. 231-243

Birch, M.C. & Haynes, K.F., *Insect Pheromones*, Edward Arnold, London, 1982

Boland, C.R.J., Heinsohn, R., and Cockburn, A. Deception by helpers in cooperatively breeding white-winged choughs and its experimental manipulation, *Behavioural Ecology & Sociobiology* (1997), Vol. 41, no. 4, pp. 251-256

Boswall, J. The Language of Bird, *Proceedings of the Royal Institution* (1983), Vol. 5, Science Reviews Ltd, pp. 249-303.

Brown, C.H. Ventroloquial and locatable vocalizations in birds. *Z. Tierpsychol* 1982, Vol. 59, no. 4, pp. 338-350.

Byrne, Richard, W. & Whiten, Andrew. Computation and Mindreading in Primate Tactical Deception. *Natural Theories of Mind. Evolution, Development & Simulation of Everyday Mindreading* (Whiten, Andrew ed.), Basil Blackwell, Oxford, 1991.

Capra, Fritjof. Knowing that We Know. *The Web of Life*, Harper Collins, London 1996, pp. 278-288.

Carlson, A.D. *et al.* Flash communication between the sexes of the firefly, *Photuris lucicrescens*. *Physiological Entomology* (1982), Vol 7, pp. 127-132.

Cheney, D.L. & Seyfarth, R. M. *How Monkeys See the World*, University of Chicago Press, Chicago 1990.

Chomsky, N. *Language and Mind*, Harcourt, Brace, Jovanovich, New York, 1972.

Clark, A.B. Scent marks as social signals in *Galago crassicaudatus*. II Discrimination between individuals by scent. *Journal of Chemical Ecology* (1982), Vol. 8, p. 8

Conner, W.E. Un Chant. D'Appel Amoureux: Acoustic communication in moths. *Journal of Experimental Biology* (1999), Vol. 202, pp. 1711-1723

Okl, A. *et al.* The structure and function of songs emitted by southern green stink bugs from Brazil, Florida, Italy and Slovenia. *Physiological Entomology* (2000), Vol. 25, pp. 196-205

Okl, A. *et al.* Temporal and spectral properties of the songs of the southern green stink bug *Nezara viridula* (L) from Slovenia. *European Journal of Physiology* 439 (2000), pp.168-170

Converse, L. J. *et al.* Communication of ovulatory state to mates by female pygmy marmosets, *Cebuella pygmaea*. *Animal Behaviour*, 49 (1995), pp. 615-621

Cooper, K. An instance of delayed communication in solitary wasps. *Nature*, 178 (1956), pp. 601-602

Crook, J.H, On attributing consciousness to animals. *Nature* 303: 5912 (1983), pp.11-14

Decker, Denise M. *et al.* Lipid components in anal scent sacs of three mongoose species, *Helogale parvula, Crossarchus obscurus, Suricata suricatta*. *Journal of Chemical Ecology*, 18: 9 (1992)

Eisenberg, J.F. & Kleiman, D. G. Olfactory communication in mammals. *Annual Review of Ecology and Systematics*, 3 (1972), pp. 1-31

Elowson, A. *et al.* Ontogeny of trill and J-call vocalizations in the pygmy marmoset, *Cebuella pygmaea*. *Animal Behaviour*, 43 (1992), pp. 703-715

Epple, G., Kuederling, I. and Belcher, A. Some communicatory functions of scent marking in the cotton-top tamarin (*Saguinus oedipus oedipus*). *Journal of Chem Ecol* 1988, Vol. 14, no. 2, pp. 503-516

Estes, R.D. *The Behaviour Guide to African Mammals*, University of California Press, Berkeley & Los Angeles, California, USA, 1991

Falls, J.B., *et al.* Song matching in the great tit (*Parus major*): the effect of similarity and familiarity. *Animal Behaviour*, 30 (1982), pp. 997-1009

Fine, M. L. *et al.* Communication in fishes. *How Animals Communicate*, Thomas A. Sebeok (ed.), Indiana University Press, Bloomington & London, 1977

Gemeno, C. *et al.* Aggressive chemical mimicry by the bolas spider *Mastophora hutchinsoni*: identification and quantification of a major prey's sex pheromone components in the spider's volatile emissions. *Journal of Chemical Ecology*, 26: 5 (2000)

Gittleman, John L. (ed.), *Carnivore behaviour, ecology and evolution*, Chapman & Hall, London, 1989

Gonzalez, Guillermo, *et al.* Immunocompetence and condition-dependent sexual advertisement in male house sparrows (*Passer domesticus*). *Journal of Animal Ecology*, 68 (1999), pp. 1225-1234

Goodall, Jane. *The Chimpanzees of Gombe. Patterns of Behaviour*, Belknap Press, Harvard, 1986.

Gorman, M. and Trowbridge, B. The Role of Odour in the Social Lives of Carnivores. *Carnivore behavior, ecology, and evolution*, John L. Gittleman (ed), Chapman and Hall, London, 1989

Gray, J.A.B., & Denton, E.J. Fast pressure pulses and communication between fish. *Journal of the Marine Biological Association of the United Kingdom*, 71 (1991), pp. 83-106

Gray, Patricia M. *et al.* The music of nature and the nature of music, *Science*, 291 (2001), 52-54

Griffin, Donald R. *Animal Thinking*, Harvard University Press, Cambridge, Mass., 1984

Hagen, Heinrich-Otto von. Visual and acoustic display in *Uca mordax* and *Uca burgersi*, sibling species of neotropical fiddler crabs. II. Vibration signals. *Behaviour*, 91: 1-3 (1984), pp. 204-227

Hall, K.C. and Hanlon, R.T., 2001. Principal features of the mating system of a large spawning aggregation of the giant Australian cuttlefish *Sepiaapama* (Mollusca: Cephalopoda). *Marine Biology*, 2002, Vol. 140 (3)

Hanlon, R.T. & Messenger, J.B. *Cephalopod Behaviour*. Cambridge University Press, Cambridge, 1996

Harrington, Fred H, & Mech, L David. Wolf howling and its role in territory maintenance. *Behaviour*, LXVIII (1978), 207-221

Harrington, Fred H. & Mech, L. David. Wolf pack spacing: howling as a territory-independent spacing mechanism in a territorial population. *Behavioral Ecology and Sociobiology*, 12 (1983), pp. 161-168

Harrington, Fred H. Aggressive howling in wolves. *Animal Behaviour*, Vol. 35 (1987), pp. 7-12

Hauser, Marc D. How infant vervet monkeys learn to recognise starling alarm calls. *Behaviour*, Vol. 105 (1988a), pp. 187-201.

Hauser, Marc D. Ontonogenic changes in the comprehension and production of vervet monkey (*Cercopithecus aethiops*) vocalisations. *Journal of Comparative Psychology*, (1989), Vol. 103, pp. 149-158

Hauser, Marc D. *The Evolution of Communication*, Massachusetts Institute of Technology, Mass., (1993)

Hauser, Marc D. Right hemisphere dominance for the production of facial expression in monkeys. *Science*, 261 (1993), pp. 475-477

Haynes, Kenneth F. & Yeargan, Kenneth V. Exploitation of Intraspecific Communication Systems: Illicit Signalers and Receivers. *Annals of the Entomological Society of America*, 92: 6 (1999), pp. 960-970

Hebets, E.A. and Uetz, G.W. Leg ornamentation and the efficacy of courtship display in four species of wolf spider (Araneae: Lycosidae). *Behavioral Ecology & Sociobiology*, 2000, Vol. 47, no. 4, pp. 280-286

Hebets, E.A. and Uetz, G.W. Female responses to isolated signals from multimodal male courtship displays in the wolf spider genus Schizocosa (Araneae: Lycosidae). *Animal Behaviour*, 1999, Vol. 57, no. 4, pp. 865-872

Heinrich, B. & Marzluff, J.M. Do common ravens yell because they want to attract others? *Behavioral Ecology and Sociobiology*, 28 (1991), pp. 13-21

Herring, P.J. Species abundance, sexual encounter and bioluminescent signalling in the deep sea. *Phil. Trans. Royal Society, London, B*, 355, (2000), pp. 1273-1276

Hinde, R.A. & Rowell, T.E. Communication by postures and facial expressions in the Rhesus Monkey (*Macaca mulatta*). *Proceedings of the Zoological Society of London*, 138 (1962), pp. 1-21

Hölldobler, Bert & Wilson, E.O., *Journey to the Ants: A Story of Scientific Exploration*, Belknap Press, Harvard University Press, Cambridge, Mass., USA, 1994

Hölldobler, Bert & Wilson, Edward G. Queen Control in Colonies of Weaver Ants, *Hymenoptera: Formicidae. Annals of the Entomological Society of America*, 76: 2 (1983)

Holmes, W. The colour changes and colour patterns of *Sepia officinalis* L. *Proceedings of the Zoological Society of London*, 1940. A 110, pp. 2-35

Hopkins, Carl D. Electric communication in fish. *American Scientist*, Vol. 62, (1974a), pp. 426-437

Hudson, Robyn, & Vodermayer, Thomas. Spontaneous and odour-induced chin marking in domestic female rabbits. *Animal Behaviour*, 43 (1992), pp. 329-336

Insley, Stephen J. Mother-offspring vocal recognition in northern fur seals is mutual but asymmetrical. *Animal Behaviour*, 60 (2000), 1-9 (Also in: *Animal Behaviour*, 61 (2001), pp.129-137

Insley, Stephen J. Long-term vocal recognition in the northern fur seal. *Nature*, 406 (2000)

Insley, Stephen J. Mother-offspring separation and acoustic stereotypy: a comparison of call morphology in two species of pinnipeds. *Behavior*, 120: 1-2 (1992), pp. 103-122

Janik, V.M. Whistle matching in wild bottlenose dolphins (*Tursiops truncatus*). *Science*, 2000, Vol. 289, pp. 1355-1357

Jouventin, Pierre, *et al*, Finding a parent in a king penguin colony: the acoustic system of individual recognition. *Animal Behaviour*, 57 (1999), 1175-1183

Kappeler, P. M. Social status and scent marking in *Lemur catta*. *Animal Behaviour*, 40 (1990)

Kimball, Rebecca T. Female choice for Male Morphological Traits in House Sparrows, *Passer domesticus*. *Ethology*, 102 (1996), pp. 639-648

Kinyon, D. Badis Badis. *Delta Tale (A bi-monthly publication of*

Potomac Valley Aquarium Society), 30 (2001), 2-3

Kloubec, Bohuslav & Apek, Jr, Miroslav. Diurnal, nocturnal, and seasonal patterns of singing activity in marsh warblers. *Biologia*, Bratislava, 55: 2 (2000), pp.185-193

Krebs, John R. The significance of song repertoires: The Beau Geste Hypothesis. *Animal Behaviour* (1977), Vol. 25: 475-478

Krebs, John R. & Dawkins, Richard. Animal Signals: Information or Manipulation? *Behavioural Ecology*, Blackwell Scientific Publications, Oxford, (1978)

Krebs, John R. & Kroodsma, Donald E. Repertoires and geographical variation in bird song. *Advances in the Study of Behavior,* Vol. 11, Academic Press, Inc., 1980

Krebs, John R. *et al.* Song matching in the great tit (*Parus major*). *Animal Behaviour*, Vol. 29 (1981), pp. 918-923

Kricher, John. Manakins. *A Neotropical Comparison*, Princeton University Press, 1997

Kruuk, Hans, *et al.* Scent-marking with the subcaudal gland by the European badger, *Meles meles* L. *Animal Behaviour*, Vol. 32 (1984), pp. 899-907

Langbauer Jr, William R. *et al.* Responses of captive African elephants to playback of low-frequency calls. *Canadian Journal of Zoology*, Vol. 67 (1989), pp. 2604-2607

Lariviere, Serge & Messier, François. Aposematic behaviour in the striped skunk. *Ethology,* Vol. 102 (1996)

Lengagne, Thierry, *et al.* How do king penguins (*Aptenodytes patagonicus*) apply the mathematical theory of information to communicate in windy conditions. *Proceedings of the Royal Society, London, B*, Vol. 266 (1999), pp. 1623-1628

Lewis, Edwin & Narins, Peter. Do frogs communicate with seismic signals? *Science,* Vol. 227 (1985)

Losey, George S. *et al.* Cleaning symbiosis between the wrasse, *Thalassoma duperry*, and the green turtle, *Chelonia mydas*. *Copeia*, Vol. 3 (1994), pp. 684-690

Marler, Peter. Subsong and plastic song: Their role in the vocal learning process. *Acoustic Communication in Birds* (eds Kroodsma, D. Miller, E. Ouellet, H.), Academic Press, New York (1982), pp. 25-50.

Marler, Peter & Evans, Christopher. Bird calls: just emotional displays or something more? *IBIS*, Vol. 138 (1996), pp. 26-33.

Marshall, N.J. Cronin T.W. and Osorio, D. *Colour communication and the bright colours of coral reef animals: who sees them and why?* 6th International Behavioural Ecology Congress Abstract, Australian National University, Canberra, 1996.

Masters, W. Mitch. Vibrations in the orbwebs of *Nuctenea sclopetaria* (Araneidae). *Behavioral Ecology and Sociobiology*, Vol. 15 (1984), pp. 207-215.

Maturana, Humberto and Francisco Varela. *The Tree of Knowledge*. Shambhala, Boston, 1987

Maynard-Smith, J. The evolution of alarm calls. *American Naturalist* (1965), Vol. 99, pp. 59-63.

McComb, Karen. Playback as a tool for studying contests between social groups. P.K. McGregor (*ed.*), *Playback and Studies of Animal Communication*, Plenum Press, New York, 1992.

McComb, Karen, *et al.* Unusually extensive networks of vocal recognition in African elephants. *Animal Behaviour*, 59 (2000), pp. 1103-1109.

McComb, Karen, *et al.* Matriarchs as repositories of social knowledge in African elephants. *Science*, 292 (2001), pp. 491-494.

McComb, Karen, *et al.* Long-distance communication of social identity in African elephants (submitted to A*nimal Behaviour* 2002)

McRobert, Scott P. & Bradner, Joshua. The influence of body coloration on shoaling preferences in fish. *Animal Behaviour*, Vol. 56 (1998), pp. 611-615.

Michelson, A. The transfer of information in the dance language of honeybees: progress and problems. *Journal of Comparative Physiology A (*1993), Vol. 173, pp. 135-141.

Middendorf III, George A. & Sherbrooke, Wade C. Canid elicitation of blood-squirting in a horned lizard (*Phrynosoma cornutum*). *Copeia*, 2 (1992)

Mills, M.G.L., & Gorman, M.L. The scent-marking behaviour of the spotted hyaena *Crocuta crocuta* in the southern Kalahari. *Journal of Zoology*, London, 212 (1987), pp. 483-497

Minta, Steven C. Sexual differences in spatio-temporal interaction among badgers. *Oecologia* 96 (1993), pp. 402-409

Moeller, A.P. Badge size in the house sparrow, *Passer domesticus*. Effects of intra- and intersexual selection. *Behavioral Ecology and Sociobiology*, 22 (1988), pp. 373-378

Morin, James G. Firefleas of the sea: luminescent signalling in marine ostracode crustaceans. *Florida Entomologist*, 69: 1 (1986), pp.105-121

Morton, E. On the occurrence and significance of motivational-structural rules in some bird and mammal sounds. *American Naturalist* (1977), Vol. 111, pp. 855-869

Neudecker, Stephen. Eye camouflage and false eyespots: chaetodontid responses to predators. *Environmental Biology of Fishes*, 25: pp.1-3, (1989)

Noad, M.J., Cato, D.H., Bryden, M.M., Jenner, M.N., Jenner, K.C.S. Cultural revolution in whale songs. *Nature,* 2000. Vol. 408, no. 6812, p. 537

Osorio-Beristain, Marcela & Drummond, Hugh. Non-aggressive mate guarding by the blue-footed booby: balance of female and male control. *Behavioral Ecology and Sociobiology*, 43 (1998), pp. 307-315

Payne, Katharine B. *et al.* Infrasonic calls of the Asian elephant (*Elephas maximus*). *Behavioral Ecology and Sociobiology*, 18 (1986), pp. 297-301

Pigozzi, Giorgio. Latrine use and the function of territoriality in the European badger, *Meles meles*, in a Mediterranean coastal habitat. *Animal Behaviour*, 39: 5 (1990), pp. 1000-1002

Poole, J.H. Signals and assessment in African elephants: evidence from playback experiments. *Animal Behaviour* (1999), Vol. 58, no. 1, pp. 185-193

Poole, J.H., Payne, K., Langbauer, W.R., Jr., Moss, C.J. The social contexts of some very low frequency calls of African elephants. *Behavioral Ecology & Sociobiology* (1988), Vol. 22, no. 6, pp. 385-392

Randall, Jan A. & Matocq, Marjorie D. Why do kangaroo rats (*Dipodomys spectabilis*) footdrum at snakes?. *Behavioral Ecology* 8: 4 (1996), pp. 404-413

Rich, Tracey J., & Hurst, Jane L. Scent marks as reliable signals of the competitive ability of mates. *Animal Behaviour*, 56 (1998), pp. 727-735

Richardson, Douglas. *Big Cats*, Whittet Books, London, 1992

Roces, Flavio, & Hölldobler, Bert. Vibrational communication between hitchhikers and foragers in leaf-cutting ants (*Atta cephalotes*). *Behavioral Ecology and Sociobiology*, 37 (1995), pp. 297-302

Roper, T.J., *et al.* Territorial marking with faeces in badgers (*Meles meles*). *Behaviour*, 127: 3–4 (1993)

Rudnai, Judith A., *The Social Life of the Lion*, Medical and Technical Publishing Co. Ltd, 1968/69

Rumbaugh, Duane M., & Gill, Timothy V. The learning skills of great apes. *Journal of Human Evolution* 2 (1973), 171-179 (Paper presented at the NATO Advanced Study Institute on comparative Biology of Primates, Turin, Italy, 1972)

Salmon, Michael. Waving display and sound production in the courtship behavior of *Uca pugilator*, with comparisons to *Uca minax* and *Uca pugnax*. *Zoologica: New York Zoological Society*, 50: 12 (1965), pp.123-149

Schneider, D. The sex-attractant receptor in moths. *Scientific American*, Vol. 231: 1 (1974), pp. 28-35

Schüch, Wolfgang & Barth, Friedrich. Vibratory communication in a spider: female responses to synthetic male vibrations. *Journal of Comparative Physiology A* 166 (1990), 817-826

Scott, Jonathan & Angela, *Mara-Serengeti: a photographer's paradise*, Fountain Press, Faringdon, Oxfordshire, 2000

Sebeok, Thomas, A. (ed.) *How Animals Communicate*, Indiana University Press, Ind. (1977)

Seeley, T.D., Mikheyes, A.S., Pagano. G.J. Dancing bees tune both duration and rate of waggle-run production in relation to nectar-source profitability. *Journal of Comparative Physiology A* (2000), Vol. *186*: pp. 813-819

Seyfarth, Robert, *et al.* Monkey responses to three different alarm calls: Evidence of predator classification and semantic communication. *Science*, 210 (1980)

Sillén-Tullberg, B. Higher survival of an aposematic than of a cryptic form of a distasteful bug. *Oecologia*, 67 (1985), pp. 411-415

Simmons, R.B. and Conner, W.E. Ultrasonic Signals in the Defense and Courtship of *Euchaetes egle* and *E. bolteri* (Lepidoptera, Arctiidae). *J. Insect Behavior*, 1996, Vol. 9, pp. 909-919

Simpson, S.J., *et al.* Gregarious behavior in desert locusts is evoked by touching their back legs. *Proceedings of the National Academy of Science, USA*, 98:7 (2001), pp. 3895-3897

Slobodchikoff, C.N., *et al.* Semantic information distinguishing individual predators in the alarm calls of Gunnison's prairie dogs. *Animal Behaviour*, 42 (1991), pp. 713-719

Smith, James L. David, *et al.* Scent-marking in free-ranging tigers, *Panthera tigris*. *Animal Behaviour*, 37 (1989), pp. 1-10

Smolker, Rachel, & Pepper, John W. Whistle convergence among allied male bottlenose dolphins (Delphinidae, *Tursiops* sp.). *Ethology*, 105 (1999), pp.595-617

Snowdon, Charles T., & Pola, Yvonne V. Interspecific and intraspecific responses to synthesized pygmy marmoset vocalizations. *Animal Behaviour*, 26 (1978), pp. 192-206

Snowdon, Charles T. Language capacities of non-human animals. *Yearbook of Physical Anthropology*, 33 (1990), pp. 215-243

Sonerud, Geir A. To distract display or not: grouse hens and foxes. *OIKOS* 51 (1988), pp. 233-237

Stafford, Kathleen, *et al.* Long-range acoustic detection and localization of blue whale calls in the northeast Pacific Ocean. *Journal of the Acoustic Society of America*, 104: 6 (1998), pp. 3616-3625

Stirling, Ian, *Polar Bears*, University of Michigan Press, 1988

Stowe, Mark K., *et al.* The chemistry of eavesdropping, alarm and deceit. *Proceedings of the National Academy of Science, USA*, 92 (colloquium paper, 1995), pp. 23-28

Tautz, Jürgen, *et al.* Use of a sound-based vibratome by leaf-cutting ants. *Science* 267 (1995), pp. 84-87

Thomas, R.J., Székely, T., Cuthill, I.C., Harper, D.G.C., Newson, S.E., Frayling, T. and Wallis, P. Eye size in birds and the timing of song at dawn. *Proceedings of the Royal Society*, Series B, in press 2002

Trainer, J.M., McDonald, D.B. Singing performance, frequency matching and courtship success of long-tailed manakins (*Chiroxiphia linearis*). *Behavioral Ecology & Sociobiology*, 1995, Vol. 37, no. 4, pp. 249-254

Valone, Thomas J. Food-associated calls as public information about patch quality. *OIKOS* 77 (1996), pp. 153-157

Vince, Margaret A. Tactile communication between ewe and lamb and the onset of suckling. *Behaviour*, 101 (1987), pp.156-176

Vincent, Amanda C.J., & Sadler, Laila M. Faithful pair bonds in wild seahorses, *Hippocampus whitei*. *Animal Behaviour*, 50 (1995), pp. 1557-1559

Waser, Peter M., & Brown, Charles H. Is there a 'sound window' for primate communication. *Behavioral Ecology and Sociobiology*, 15 (1984), pp. 73-76

Waser, Peter M., & Brown, Charles H. Habitat acoustics and primate communication. *American Journal of Primatology*,

10 (1986), pp.135-154

Watson, Sheree L., *et al*. Scent-marking and cortisol response in the small-eared bush-baby (*Otolemur garnettii*). *Physiology & Behaviour*, 66: 4 (1999), pp. 695-699

Weygoldt, Peter. Mating and spermatophore morphology in whip spiders. *Zoologischer Anzeiger* 236 (1997/98), pp. 259-276

Wilson, E.O. *The insect societies*. Cambridge, MA: Harvard University Press, 1971

Wood, William F. The History of Skunk Defensive Secretion Research. *The Chemical Educator*, 5: 3 (2000)

Woodmansee, Katya B. *et al*. Scent marking (pasting) in a colony of immature spotted hyaenas, *Crocuta crocuta*: a developmental study. *Journal of Comparative Psychology*, 105: 1 (1991)

Yamagiwa, Juichi. Functional analysis of social staring behavior in an all-male group of mountain gorillas. *Primates*, 33: 4 (1992), pp. 523-544

Yanagisawa, Yasunobu. Studies on the interspecific relationship between gobiid fish and snapping shrimp. II. Life history and pair formation of snapping shrimp, *Alpheus bellulus*. *Publications of the Seto Marine Biological Laboratory*, XXIX: 1-3 (1984), pp. 93-116

Zimmermann, Elke. Aspects of reproduction and behavioral and vocal development in Senegal bush-babies (*Galago senegalensis*). *International Journal of Primatology*, 10: 1 (1989)

Picture Acknowledgements

© Bryan & Cherry Alexander 127. © Scott Alexander 138. © Ardea/M.Watson i; John Mason 16; A. Greensmith 69; Ron & Valerie Taylor 111; P. Morris 176,180; Hans & Judy Beste 220. © Bruce Coleman Collection/Tero Niemi 31; Pacific Stock 52-53, 54; John Cancalosi 59; Hans Reinhard 65; Orion Press 107; Kim Taylor 124,198-199; Gunter Ziesler 168 above,204; Bob & Clara Calhoun 189; Marie Read 207; Johnny Johnson 212; Staffan Widstrand 213; Gerald S. Cubitt 235; Joe McDonald 236. © Corbis/Kevin Schafer 79 centre. © Monika & Hans D.Dossenbach 23, 97. © Georgette Douwma 48, 90, 92, 246. © H. Carl Gerhardt 57. © Jane Goodall Institute 41, 100 above. © Images of Africa/Carla Signorini Jones 165. © Frank Lane Picture Agency/W. Wisniewski 24-25; Christiana Carvalho 63; Geoff Moon 72; Martin Withers 79 above right: Terry Whittaker 79 above left,101,231 below; L.West 82 above; Mindon Pictures 161; S.Charlie Brown 173 below; Wendy Dennis 231 above; Flip de Nooyer 240-241. © Natural History Photographic Agency/Iain Green 8; Andy Rouse 12,95; Henry Ausloos 47; David Watts 120; Jonathan & Angela Scott 144,150; Dr Ivan Polunin 156; Christophe Ratier 162-163; Kevin Schafer 168 below,206; Fredy Mercay 192 above; Anthony Bannister 231 right; Stephen Dalton 244. © Natural Visions/Peter David 112; Heather Angel 113. © Nature Photographers Ltd/Barry R. Hughes 80 (Chaffinch); Paul Sterry 80 (Greenfinch),115. © Nature Picture Library (incorporating BBC Natural History Unit Picture Library)/Pete Oxford ii-iii; Bernard Walton 18; Jeff Rotman 20,74,76; Michael Pitts 21; David Kjaer 22,85; Karl Amman 28; Brandon Cole 55,223; T. Andrewartha endpapers, 64-65; Dietmar Nill 80 (Goldfinch); Tom Vezo 82 below; Anup Shah 79 below left, 83,142; Martin Dohrn 88-89; Miles Barton 104 below right; David Shale 109; Jurgen Freund 116; Peter Blackwell 119; Richard Kirby 123; Torsten Brehm 136; Jeff Foott 137,217; Bruce Davidson 143; Simon King 145; Kevin J. Keatley 152; Mike Wilkes 170; Sarah Byatt 173 centre; Rod Williams 210; Tony Heald 226. © Michael Neugebauer/mine@netway.at 104 above left. © Oxford Scientific Films/Ray Richardson 14; Konrad Wothe 40; Mark Webster 45; Howie Garber 62; Doug Allan 76; Max Gibbs 77; Manfred Pfefferle 80 (Hawfinch); Mark Hamblin 80 (Bullfinch); Rudie H. Kuiter 81; Clive Bromhall 100 below,104 below left; Martyn Colbeck 103; Jackie Le Fevre 104 above right; Judd Cooney 129; Daniel J. Cox 134; Anthony Bannister 147; Richard Packwood 149; G. I. Bernard 173 above; Fredrik Ehrenstrom 175; James H. Robinson 192 below,238; Bertram G. Murray Jr 234; Raymond A. Mendez 237. © Premaphotos Wildlife/K. G. Preston-Mafham 131,194-195,209,229. © Science Photo Library/Andrew Syred 155; Jack K. Clark 182 below; Hermann Eisenbeiss 186. © Still Pictures/M & C Denis-Huot 36,79 below right; Peter Weimann 60; Roland Seitre 128; Muriel Nicolotti 166. © Woodfall Wild Images/Mike Powles 104 centre right; Bob Gibbons 158.

Graphics by Jan Golunski © Jelly Television Ltd, Bristol: 17; 34-35 photo © Steve Bloom Images; 140-141 photo © Natural History Photographic Agency/Daniel Heuclin; 178 photo © Bruce Coleman Collection/Jane Burton; 182 above,centre and below right.

Charts by Jeremy Ashcroft: 67, 179, 184, 200.

Index

Figures in *italics* indicate captions.